GW00570841

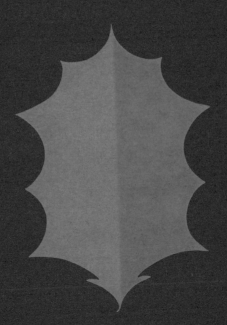

THE
GALLIARD
BOOK
OF
CAROLS

THE
GALLIARD
BOOK
OF
CAROLS

Stainer & Bell

First published in 1980
by
Stainer & Bell Ltd

ISBN 0 85249 584 6

Preface

Most of the 130 carols are selected from a large collection made from many sources, at the request of the publishers, by June Tillman. To these are added new carols specially written for the book to fill in gaps in the seasons such as Easter, Whitsuntide and Autumn when there were not many older carols to be found; there are also carols on new subjects such as the Herb Carol, a Concertgoers' Carol, and Mole End Carol. The aim is to provide a comprehensive carol book from all periods of history, beginning in the fifteenth century, and from many countries.

Texts

The choice of carols on literary grounds was finally made, in co-operation with June Tillman, by Bernard Braley, who has commissioned well-known poets to write new verses and provided some versions himself. The carols are grouped under four headings:

Christmas

Chronicles

Crucifixion

Customs

Naturally, the largest group is for Christmas. These begin with Christmas itself and go through to New Year's Eve. The section called 'Chronicles' deals with settings of stories from the Bible (including the events from Christmas to Easter), from historians, from folk tales and from modern storytellers. The story of the Crucifixion is told in carol form from the betrayal of Christ by Judas to the day of the Resurrection. The group called 'Customs' are mainly secular carols celebrating the seasons and nature, with some for feast-days such as Shrove Tuesday and others recording—with explanations—customs such as house decorating for Candlemas, May Day dancing, Hallow'een and Bonfire Night, lighting candles for Advent and the newly-revived Christingle custom.

Where French, German or Latin carols are well-known in their own language, the original is given and many have new translations or English versions. Archaic words are explained in footnotes and, in some difficult cases, a pronunciation is suggested.

A full list of poets and translators will be found on page 246. Every effort has been made to trace all owners of copyright; if any have unwittingly remained undiscovered, the publishers offer apologies and will gladly make acknowledgement in future editions.

Music

Carols by individual composers from all periods of history are printed in their original form. The medieval carols are based on the transcriptions first made by John Stevens in his famous volume in the *Musica Britannica* series, arranged for easier performance by today's compass of voices. Traditional tunes have been newly arranged by June Tillman and Allen Percival. Most of the arrangements are made so that the carols may be sung with keyboard *or* guitar, by solo voices or groups of any vocal combination; many have optional parts for instruments, singing descants or vocal backing for a soloist. The arrangers hope that performers will return to the old practice of adding instruments to voices, which was common in all carolling until the beginning of this century. In any group, at home, in conference, or at school, instruments using the bass clef can usually double the bass, treble-clef instruments can double soprano parts and violas can be happy with either alto or tenor. Percussion instruments can be added with good effect to many carols, emphasising their dancing origin, as suggested in the first carol in the book. Carolling should seldom be limited to singers. A full list of composers and arrangers will be found on page 246. Every effort has been made to trace all owners of copyright; if any have unwittingly remained undiscovered, the publishers offer apologies and will gladly make full acknowledgement in future editions.

Illustrations

The drawings are by Rachel Percival, who has based them on carol subjects treated by early painters and sculptors in many parts of Europe. Sources include 6th century mosaic, Sant'Apollinare in Classe (p. 71); 12th century sculpture, Iona (p.197); 12th century stained glass, Chartres (p. 188); 12th century wood sculpture, Brunswick (p.185); 13th century illumination, Berlin (p.125); 13th century bronze relief, Monreale (p. 211); 16th century sculpture, Warsaw (p. 81); and 17th century prints, Paris (p. 131).

* * * * * * *

All carol collections owe much to earlier compilers, from the medieval scribes whose work is now in college libraries to the nineteenth-century clerics who 're-invented' the carol and to the devoted work of re-discovering folk carols begun by Vaughan Williams and his companions in the 1920s. Wherever practicable, the 'composed' carols in this book are based on the original words and music. Only carols known as 'traditional' are given versions more suited to the 1980s. The editors hope that in re-discovering old carols, meeting new ones, and giving renewed life to the well-loved, traditional carols, this book will take its place beside the most popular of earlier collections.

Christmas

1

WE WISH YOU A MERRY CHRISTMAS

Anonymous

Traditional English

This carol may be sung in unison with keyboard or with guitar. Two-part choirs may sing the top two parts unaccompanied or with piano; SAB sing parts as shown. Tambourine or bells may play the rhythm ♩ ♩ throughout and a drum may beat the rhythm of the words in the chorus.

1 We wish you a merry Christmas (*three times*)
And a happy New Year.
Good tidings we bring
To you and your kin,
We wish you a merry Christmas,
And a happy New Year.

2 Now bring us some figgy pudding
And bring some out here.
CHORUS

3 We all like our figgy pudding
With all its good cheer.
CHORUS

4 We won't go until we've got some
So bring some out here.
CHORUS

Optional instruments

2

THIS ENDRIS NIGHT

Anonymous, fifteenth century,
modernised spelling

English, sixteenth century

© 1980 Stainer & Bell Ltd

All verses are sung to this tune, fitting the words with as little strain as possible. The top and bottom parts are given as they appear in Royal Appendix 58, British Library. In that manuscript the tune is in the tenor with alto above and bass below. This version may be sung an octave lower by TBarB or by two voices and an instrument, or as a solo with two instruments, or with guitar in D major.

> *Lullay, my child, and weep no more,*
> *Sleep and be now still,*
> *The king of bliss thy father is,*
> *As it was his will.*

1 This endris night I saw a sight,
  A maid a cradle keep,
  And ever she sang and said among
  'Lullay, my child, and sleep.'
  CHORUS

2 'I may not sleep, but I may weep,
  I am so woebegone;
  Sleep I would, but I am cold
  And clothës have I none.'
  CHORUS

3 'Me thought I heard,' the child answered,
  And to his mother he said,
  'My mother dear, what do I here,
  In crib why am I laid?'
  CHORUS

4 'I was born and laid before
  Beasts, both ox and ass.
  My mother mild, I am thy child,
  But He my Father was.'
  CHORUS

3

CHRISTMAS CANDLE

Donald Swann (1923—)

Traditional Russian
Arranged by Donald Swann (1923—)

All night long I shall burn my Christ-mas can - dle, Watch the flame bur-ning yel - low, grey and blue.

3

4

shi-ning Christ-mas can - dle, Oh shine your light so my eyes can see a-new.

All night long I shall burn my Christ-mas can - dle, I shall

5

All night long I shall
watch till the wax has all burned through.

burn my Christ-mas can-dle, I shall watch till the wax has all burned
through.

Burn my heart,
Burn my heart, my shi-ning Christ-mas can-dle, Oh
Burn my heart, my shi-ning Christ-mas can-dle, Oh

6

Solo

Burn my
shine your____ light so my heart can burn a - new.
mm ____

heart, my shi - ning Christ-mas can - dle, Oh shine your light so my

In this carol, the guitar chords are provided so that verses may be sung in unison in the key of E minor, without piano.

8

4

NOËL, RAISE THE ROOF

English version by Bernard A Braley (1924–) *Traditional French (Noël Nouvelet)*

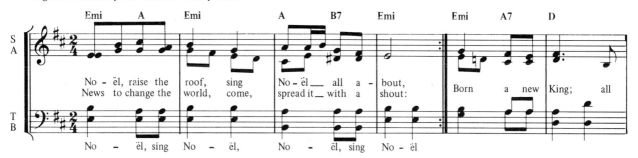

Noël, raise the roof, sing / News to change the world, come, No-ël, raise the roof, sing / spread it with a shout: Born a new King; all
No-ël, sing No-ël, No-ël, sing No-ël

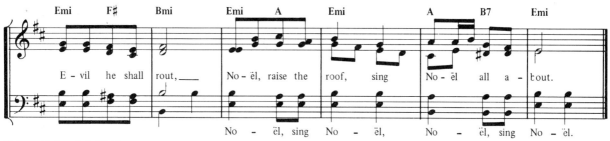

E-vil he shall rout,___ No-ël, raise the roof, sing No-ël all about.
No-ël, sing No-ël, No-ël, sing No-ël.

1 Noël, raise the roof, sing Noël all about,
   News to change the world, come, spread it with a shout:
   Born a new King; all Evil he shall rout,
   Noël, raise the roof, sing Noël all about.

2 Shepherds, seek the Christ-child, leave your ewe and ram,
   Born a human child, with us the great I AM,
   Brother from heav'n to bless the race of Man,
   Noël, raise the roof, sing out to ev'ry clan.

3 Parents of King Jesus, look into this face,
   In your trust there rests the Saviour of our race,
   Destined for Lordship here and ev'ry place,
   Noël, raise the roof, sing out through time and space.

4 Blessed with intuition, trav'llers from abroad
   To the servant King symbolic gifts afford;
   Born death to conquer was the mighty Word,
   Noël, raise the roof, in praise of Christ the Lord.

Optional voices or instruments

This carol may be sung in unison with keyboard or with guitar. Unaccompanied verses may be sung by SA, SAB or SATB choirs as written. The optional melody may be sung by first sopranos as descant or with the written SA parts to form an unaccompanied SSA verse.

5

ON CHRISTMAS NIGHT

Traditional Sussex

Traditional Sussex
Arranged by R Vaughan Williams (1872–1958)

birth._____ When King._____ All out of dark - ness

we__ have light, Which made the an – gels sing this night. All out of dark – ness

we__ have light, Which made the an – gels sing this night: 'Glo – ry to God__ and peace__ to

rall. *a tempo*

men, Now and for ev – er-more.__ A - men.'

colla voce *a tempo*

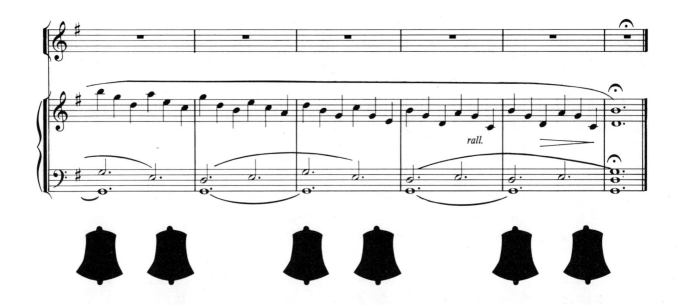

5a

THE BELLS OF ST. PAUL'S

NOTE: The following carol was written for the same tune at the request of the Dean of St. Paul's for the centenary celebration to mark the gift of the bells to the Cathedral in London, 1978. The original verse 3 has been omitted.

1 When ringers in full circle stand,
  A peal of bells at their command,
  What skill and discipline is theirs
  To call a nation to its prayers.
  'Come, come to me!' our Saviour calls:
  'Come to him!' say the Bells of St. Paul's.

2 In times of triumph, times of loss,
  The bells peal out beneath the cross;
  In joyous or in solemn sound
  They raise our spirits from the ground;
  'Come, come to me!' our Saviour calls:
  'Come to him!' say the Bells of St. Paul's.

3 God bless the ringers as they swing
  The mighty bells to make them ring,
  And God bless all who hear their tongues
  Proclaim to whom the world belongs.
  'Come, come to me!' our Saviour calls:
  'Come to him!' say the Bells of St. Paul's.

Fred Pratt Green (1903–)

6

THERE WAS A PIG (CHRISIMAS DAY)

Traditional Lancashire Children's Carol   *Traditional Lancashire*

This carol may be sung in unison or solo with keyboard or with guitar. Unaccompanied verses may be sung as written by SA, SB, SAB or SATB groups. For ATB, alto sings soprano line.

1 There was a pig went out to dig,
  Chrisimas Day, Chrisimas Day,
  There was a pig went out to dig
  On Chrisimas Day in the morning.

2 There was a cow went out to plough...

3 There was a doe went out to hoe...

4 There was a sparrow went out to harrow...

5 There was a crow went out to sow...

6 There was a minnow went out to winnow...

7 There was a sheep went out to reap...

Optional vocal or instrumental ostinato with voices

13

7

DOWN IN YON FOREST

Traditional English

Traditional Derbyshire
Arranged by R Vaughan Williams (1872–1958)

Solo or Unison

1. Down in yon for-est there stands___ a hall,
3. In___ that bed___ there lies___ a knight,} The
5. Un-der that bed___ there runs___ a flood,

The

The

bells___ of Par-a-dise I heard them ring,

It's cov-er'd all ov-er with
Whose wounds___ do bleed___ by
The one half runs wa-ter, the

Ring___

bells___ of Par-a-dise I heard them ring,

Ring___

Ring___

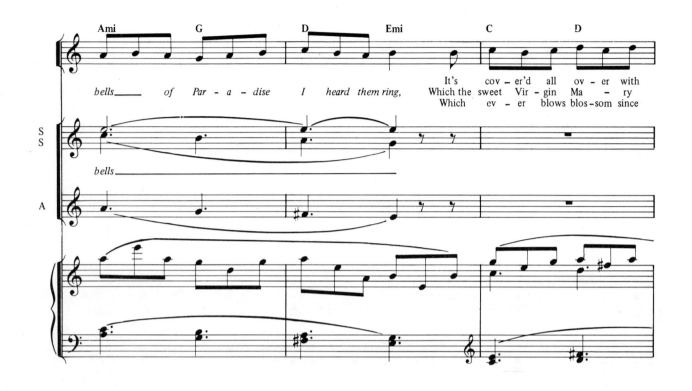

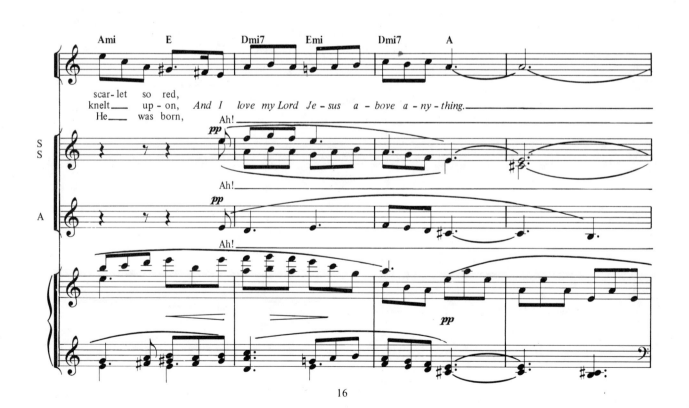

16

Guitar chords are for solo or unison use only.

8

BLESSED BE THAT MAID MARIE

G R Woodward (1848–1934)   *Traditional English*

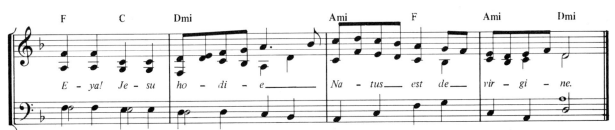

© 1980 Stainer & Bell Ltd

This carol may be sung in unison with keyboard (playing small notes) or with guitar. Unaccompanied it may be sung by SA or SAB.

1 Blessed be that maid Marie;
Born he was of her body;
Very God ere time began,
Born in time the Son of Man.   * pronounced 'yay-zoo'; 'day veer-gee-nay'
Eya! Jesu hodie
*Natus est de virgine.**

2 In a manger of an ass
Jesu lay and lullèd was;
Born to die upon the tree
Pro peccante homine.
CHORUS

3 Sweet and blissful was the song
Chanted of the angel throng,
'Peace on earth', Alleluya.
In excelsis gloria.
CHORUS

4 Fare three kings from far-off land,
Incense, gold and myrrh in hand;
In Beth'lem the Babe they see,
Stellae ducti lumine.
CHORUS

5 Make we merry on this fest,
In quo Christus natus est;
On this Child I pray you call   † = pardon
To assoil† and save us all.
CHORUS

NOTES: Eya! Jesu hodie natus est de virgine = Ah me! Jesus is born of the virgin today.   Pro peccante homine = For sinful man
In excelsis gloria = Glory in the highest   Stellae ducti lumine = Led by the light of the stars
In quo Christus natus est = When Christ was born

Reprinted by permission of A & R Mowbray Ltd.

9

MARY HAD A BOY-CHILD

Traditional Caribbean *Traditional Caribbean*

world!   Born on Chris - a - mus Day!

This carol is best sung with guitar or unaccompanied, except for bongos, maraccas and claves following the left hand rhythm (claves playing accented notes only). SSA choirs may sing the right hand part whilst keyboard (or stringed instrument) plays the bass.

Mary had a boy-child, Jeesa Chrise,
He's a-born on Chris-a-mus Day, (My, my, my, my!)
Mary had a boy-child, Jeesa Chrise,
He's a-born on Chris-a-mus Day!

1 Long time ago in Bet'-le-hem,
So de Holy Bible say,
Mary's boy-child, Jeesa Chrise,
He born on Chris-a-mus Day.

2 *CHORUS*
While shepherds watched dere flocks by night,
Them see a bright new shining star,
Then de herald choir sing,
De music seem to come from afar.

3 *CHORUS*
Now Joseph and he wife Mary,
Came to Bet'-le-hem that night,
They find no place for to born, de child;
Not a single room was in sight.

4 *CHORUS*
By-'n by they find a little nook,
In a stable all forlorn,
And in a manger cold and dark,
Mary's little boy-child was born.

5 *CHORUS*
The tree wise men tell old King Herod,
We hear a new King born today,
We bring he frankensense and myrh,
We come from far, far away.

6 *CHORUS*
When old King Herod he learned this news,
Him mad as him can be,
He tell de wise men find this child,
So that I may worship he!

CHORUS

* *CODA*
Joy to the world!
Born on Chris-a-mus Day!

*NOTE: This is a quotation from the famous hymn by Isaac Watts (1719) and the musical phrase copies that of Lowell Mason's (1839), which may in turn have been 'borrowed' from Handel's *Messiah*. The carol-hymn 'Joy to the World' is a popular Advent hymn throughout the Caribbean (and North America).

10

ADESTE FIDELES

English words by F Oakeley (1802–80)
(verse 2 by Allen Percival (1925–))

Anonymous, eighteenth century

Optional voices or instruments

Pro no - bis e - ge - num__ et__ foe - no cu - bant - em,

Pi - is__ fo - ve - a - mus am - plex - i - bus: Sic nos am -

- ant - em Quis non__ red - am - ar - et:

Ve - ni - te__ ad - o - re - mus, Do - mi - num.

1 O come, all ye faithful,
   Joyful and triumphant,
   O come ye, O come ye to Bethlehem;
   Come and behold Him,
   Born the King of angels:
   O come, let us adore Him, (*three times*)
   Christ the Lord.

2 O Mother Eternal,
   Splendours everlasting,
   See hidden under thy human form:
   Child of our Father,
   Wrapped in rags and tatters:
   CHORUS

3 God of God,
   Light of light,
   Lo, He abhors not the Virgin's womb.
   Very God,
   Begotten not created;
   CHORUS

4 See how the shepherds,
   Summoned to His cradle,
   Leaving their flocks, draw night to gaze;
   We too will thither
   Bend our joyful footsteps:
   CHORUS

5 Lo, star-led chieftains,
   Magi, Christ adoring,
   Offer Him incense, gold, and myrrh;
   We to the Christ-child
   Bring our hearts' oblations:
   CHORUS

6 Sing choirs of angels,
   Sing in exultation,
   Sing, all ye citizens of heaven above,
   'Glory to God
   In the highest':
   CHORUS

7 Yea, Lord, we greet Thee,
   Born this happy morning,
   Jesus, to Thee be glory given;
   Word of the Father,
   Now in flesh appearing:
   CHORUS

1 Adeste fideles,
   Laeti triumphantes:
   Venite, venite in Bethlehem.
   Natum videte,
   Regem Angelorum:
   Venite adoremus, (*three times*)
   Dominum.

2 Aeterni Parentis,
   Splendorem aeternum
   Velatum sub carne videbimus:
   Deum infantum,
   Pannis involutum:
   CHORUS

3 Pro nobis egenum
   Et foeno cubantem
   Piis foveamus amplexibus:
   Sic nos amantem
   Quis non redamaret:
   CHORUS

4 En grege relicto,
   Humiles ad cunas
   Vocati pastores approperant:
   Et nos ovanti
   Gradu festinemus:
   CHORUS

11

IN THE BLEAK MIDWINTER

Christina Rossetti (1830–94)

Harold Darke (1888–1976)

Lyrics (solo/unison voice):

1 In the bleak mid-win-ter, Frost-y wind made moan, Earth stood hard as ir-on, Wa-ter like a stone. Snow had fall-en, snow on snow, Snow on snow,

3 E-nough for Him, whom che-ru-bim Wor-ship night and day. A heart full of mirth, And a man-ger full of hay. E-nough for Him, whom an-gels, Fall down be-fore, The

4 What can I give Him, Poor as I am?___ If I were a shep - herd,___ I would bring a lamb.___ If I were a wise___ man, I would do my part. Yet what I can, I give___ Him, give___ my heart,___ give___ give___ my heart.

The composer originally wrote verse 1 for soprano solo and verse 3 for tenor solo. The organ (or piano with careful pedalling) may be used throughout. Verses 2 and 4 may be sung by SAB as written if no tenors available. Orchestral material and an arrangement for brass band are hired by the publishers on request.

12

THE ANGEL GABRIEL

S Baring-Gould (1834-1924)   *Traditional Basque*

This carol may be sung in unison with keyboard or with guitar in A minor. SA or SAB may be sung with or without accompaniment. Tenors and basses may use vocalise if preferred, or may follow the rhythm of the top two parts for full words.

1 The angel Gabriel from heaven came,
His wings as drifted snow, his eyes as flame;
'All hail,' said he, 'thou lowly maiden Mary,
Most highly favoured lady,'
Gloria!

3 Then gentle Mary meekly bowed her head,
'To me be as it pleaseth God,' she said,
'My soul shall laud and magnify his holy name.'
CHORUS

2 'For know a blessèd mother thou shalt be,
All generations laud and honour thee,
Thy son shall be Emmanuel, by seers foretold.
CHORUS

4 Of her, Emmanuel, the Christ, was born
In Bethlehem, all on a Christmas morn,
And Christian folk throughout the world will ever say:
CHORUS

Optional instruments

13

I SAW THREE SHIPS

Traditional English

Traditional English
Arranged by Eric Gritton (1889—)

1. I saw three ships come sail-ing in, On
4. Pray whi – ther sailed those ships all three.

Christ – mas Day, on Christ-mas Day. I saw three ships come sail – ing in. On
Pray whi – ther sailed those ships all three.

Christ – mas Day in the morn – ing.
2. And who was in those ships all three, On
5. O they sailed in to Beth – le – hem.

Christ – mas Day on Christ – mas Day, And who was in those ships all three, On
O they sailed in to Beth – le –hem,

to vv. 6-9

Christ – mas Day in the morn – ing.' 3. Our Sav – iour Christ and His La – dy, On Christ-mas Day, on

Christ – mas day, Our Sav – iour Christ and His La – dy, On Christ-mas Dáy in the morn – ing.

6 And all the bells on earth shall ring, On Christ – mas Day, on Christ – mas Day, And

clear
p

cresc.

29

all the bells on earth shall ring, On Christ-mas Day in the morn-ing.

mf

f

7 And all the an-gels in hea-ven shall sing, On Christ-mas Day on Christ-mas Day, And

S
S

pp

Optional

Ah

pp

A

all the an-gels in hea-ven shall sing, On Christ-mas Day in the morn-ing.

Ah

8. And all the souls on earth shall sing, On Christ-mas Day on Christ-mas Day, And

mf

mp

all the souls on earth shall sing, *On Christ - mas Day in the morn - ing.*

With much vigour

9. Then let us all re - joice a - main, *On Christ-mas Day, on Christ-mas Day,* Then let us all re -

-joice a - main, *On Christ-mas Day in the morn - ing.*

14

AWAY IN A MANGER

Anonymous American (1885)　　　　　　　　　　　　　　　　　*W J Fitzpatrick (1838–1921)*

A - way in a manger, no crib for a bed, The little Lord Jesus laid down his sweet head; The stars in the bright sky looked down where he lay, The little Lord Jesus asleep in the hay.

© 1980 Stainer & Bell Ltd

Guitar chords are for use only in the key of E. The arrangement may be sung in unison with piano accompaniment. Two-part choirs sing the top two parts with piano; SAB sing parts as shown. A triangle may be added on the first beat of every other bar (and on the last note).

1 Away in a manger, no crib for a bed,
  The little Lord Jesus laid down his sweet head;
  The stars in the bright sky looked down where he lay,
  The little Lord Jesus asleep on the hay.

2 The cattle are lowing, the baby awakes,
  But little Lord Jesus, no crying he makes:
  I love thee, Lord Jesus; look down from the sky,
  And stay by my side until morning is nigh.

3 Be near me, Lord Jesus; I ask thee to stay
  Close by me for ever, and love me, I pray;
  Bless all the dear children in thy tender care,
  And fit us for heaven to live with thee there.

Optional instruments

© 1980 Stainer & Bell Ltd

15

NOËL DE THEVET

Translation by Edward Bliss Reed (1872–1940)

French, eighteenth century
Arranged by David Stanley Smith (1877–1940)

pp
The – vet wait – ed in his work-shop, Work-ing till the mid –night bell, 'Christ is born to –
When he heard an – ge – lic voi – ces Joy –ous –ly the ti – dings tell: Ma – ry is his

Last verse ending, last line:

rall. e morendo

night, Mes –si – ah, Wait– ed long.
mai – den mo–ther,' Was their song.

And in leav–ing, paid o – bei-sance, Reverent–ly.

© 1927 Stainer & Bell Ltd

This carol may be sung in unison or by a choir with or without piano or guitar, lower parts singing 'la, la, la' throughout.

1 Thevet waited in his workshop,
  Working till the midnight bell,
  When he heard angelic voices
  Joyously the tidings tell:
  'Christ is born tonight, Messiah,
  Waited long,
  Mary is his maiden mother',
  Was their song.

2 Out into the street he hastened
  Wishing those gay songs to hear.
  He was thrilled with joy and gladness
  As the chorus now came near,
  For the singers were his town-folk
  Whom he knew,
  And from every nearby village
  They came too.

3 In the midst of that assembly
  Boldly then he took his stand,
  Each one telling in the singing
  Of great joy for all the land.
  From all quarters of the city
  Still they ran,
  And from every little village
  Came each man.

4 Everyone in that assembly
  Waited till the song was done
  Having learned the joyful tidings
  To their homes they went again.
  'We were happy on that morning,'
  Said each one,
  They had come and seen together
  Mary's Son.

5 Then in turn each one came forward
  By the Child his gift to place;
  Glad to be alive, they marvelled
  At his beauty, at his grace.
  Each before the Holy Family
  Bowed the knee,
  And in leaving paid obeisance
  Reverently.

NOTE: Thevet was a legendary carpenter in Burgundy, pronounced 'Tay-vay'.
© 1927 Stainer & Bell Ltd

16

THE CAROL OF THE MOUSE

Cecily Taylor (1930--)   *Richard Graves (1926—)*

1 A mouse in the straw creeps up into the hay,
And near a new baby he nestles to stay,
And there in the warmth of the peace that it brings
He shares in the sleeping of all tiny things:
Bye-lo, bye-lo,
All tiny things.

2 He wakes when the door creaks—the night wind is chill
  As in stumble peasants come down from the hill;
  He smells the new life of a lamb that they bring;
  Their eyes hold the wonder of some holy thing:
  Bye-lo, bye-lo,
  Some holy thing.

4 In darkness he wakens, hears rustling around—
  The people are leaving with hardly a sound:
  The night holds a secret, a warning it brings
  As danger treads nearer for some tiny things:
  Bye-lo, bye-lo,
  Some tiny things.

3 Then later he follows the people who find
  A home that will be of the permanent kind:
  Such visitors come there! But why should a king
  Kneel down with an offering for one baby thing?
  Bye-lo, bye-lo,
  One baby thing.

5 At dawn comes a soldier—they're searching the land—
  His eyes are as sharp as the sword in his hand:
  The mouse hears the cries, in the fear that they bring
  He flees with the terror of all tiny things:
  Bye-lo, bye-lo,
  All tiny things.

17

THE TWELVE DAYS OF CHRISTMAS

Anonymous   *Traditional English*

On the first day of Christ-mas my true love sent to me a part-ridge in a pear tree, (a pear tree). On the

se-cond day of Christ-mas my true love sent to me four co-loured birds, three French hens
third
fourth

Verses 5 to 12

two tur-tle doves, and a part-ridge in a pear tree, (a pear tree). On the ...... day of Christ-mas my

true love sent to me twelve drum-mers drum-ming, e-le-ven pi-pers pi-ping, ten lords a-leap-ing

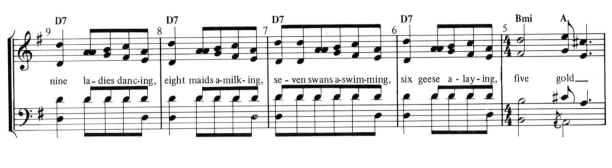

nine la-dies danc-ing, eight maids a-milk-ing, se-ven swans a-swim-ming, six geese a-lay-ing, five gold__

rings, four__ col-oured birds, three French hens, two__ tur-tle doves, and a part-ridge__ in a pear tree, (a pear tree).

In singing this 'number' carol match the days to the number of gifts by cutting during the repeats to the numbered bar for each verse. The carol may be sung in unison with piano. Two-part choirs may sing the top two parts unaccompanied or with piano; SAB sing parts as shown; SSA altos sing tenor part.

Optional instruments

Verses 2 to 4

* See note above on numbered bars.

18
WHAT TIDINGS BRINGEST THOU?

Medieval English   *Medieval English*

'What ti-dings brin-gest thou, mes - sen - ger, Of Chris - tes___ birth___ this___ Yo - lës___ day?' A babe___ is born of___ high___ na - -ture, The Prince of___ Peace___ that___ e - ver shall be; Of heaven and___ earth he___ hath___ the___ cure, His lord - ship is___ e - -ter - ni - ty: Such won - der ti - dings___ ye___ may___ hear. 'What

ti - dings bring - 'est thou mes - sen - ger?' That man ___ is ___ made now

unison v.3

D.C.

God - dës peer, Whom sin had ___ made ___ but ___ fien - dës ___ prey.

'*What tidings bringest thou, messenger,*
Of Christës birth this Yolës day?'

1 A babe is born of high nature,
   The Prince of Peace that ever shall be;
   Of heaven and earth he hath the cure,
   His lordship is eternity:
   Such wonder tidings ye may hear.
   '*What tidings bringest thou, messenger?*'
   That man is made now Goddës peer,
   Whom sin had made but fiendës prey.
   CHORUS

2 A wonder thing is now befall;
   That king that formëd star and sun,
   And heaven and earth and angels all,
   Now in mankind is new begun:
   Such wonder tidings ye may hear.
   '*What tidings bringest thou, messenger?*'
   An infant is now of one year,
   That hath been ever and shall be ay.
   CHORUS

3 That seemliest selcouth to see:
   This burd that hath this baby-born
   And lord conceived of high degree,
   A maiden is as was beforn:
   Such wonder tidings ye may hear.
   '*What tidings bringest thou, messenger?*'
   That maiden and mother is one in fere,
   And she a lady of great array.
   CHORUS

4 That loveliest gan greet her child:
   Hail Son, hail Brother, hail Father dear!
   Hail daughter, he saith, Hail mother mild!
   This hailing was on quaint manner.
   Such wonder tidings ye may hear.
   '*What tidings bringest thou, messenger?*'
   That hailing was of so good cheer
   Than mannës pain is turned to play.
   CHORUS

NOTES: selcouth = marvel   burd = maiden   in fere = together   gan = did

39

19
CRADLE SONG

Anonymous English, sixteenth century

attrib. William Byrd (?1542–1624)
Arranged by E H Fellowes (1870–1951)

My sweet lit – tle darling, my com – fort and joy, Sing lul – la-by lul – la,

My sweet lit – tle darling, my com – fort and joy, Sing lul – la-by lul – la,

My sweet lit – tle darling, my com – fort and joy, Sing lul – la-by lul – la,

In beau – ty sur – pass – ing the prin – ces of

In beau – ty sur – pass – ing the prin – ces of

In beau – ty sur – pass – ing the prin – ces of

Troy, Sing lul – la – by lul la; Now

Troy, Sing lul – la – by la lul – la; Now

Troy, Sing lul – la – by lul – la; Now

cresc.

cresc.

cresc.

poco cresc.

41

hush, child, now sleep, child, thy mo – ther's sweet boy, Sing

hush, child, now sleep,— child, thy mo – ther's sweet boy, Sing

hush, child,— now sleep, child, thy mo – ther's sweet boy, Sing

lul – la – by lul – la; The Gods bless and

lul – la – by lul – la – by lul – la; The Gods bless and

lul – la – by lul – la – by lul – la; The Gods bless and

This carol was written for a solo voice with an accompaniment of viols. For a transcription of the original, see Musica Britannica Volume 22.

20

STANDING IN THE RAIN

Sydney Carter (1915--)   Sydney Carter (1915--)

No use knock-ing on the win-dow, There is no-thing we can do, sir. All the beds are booked al-rea-dy, There is no-thing left for you, sir.

Stand-ing in the rain, / There he is a-gain, / Knock-ing on the win-dow, Knock-ing on the win-dow Knock-ing on the win-dow (On a Christ-mas / In the same old Day. way.

Day (repeat only) Stand-ing in the rain / There he is a-gain, Knock-ing on the win-dow, Knock-ing on the win-dow (On a Christ-mas / In the same old / same old way.

Reprinted by permission of Essex Music International Ltd

The verse is best sung in unison unaccompanied, in free speech rhythm, but choirs of SA, SAB or SATB may sing it as written; SSA altos sing bass an octave higher. The chorus may be accompanied by keyboard or by guitar.

1 No use knocking on the window,
There is nothing we can do, sir.
All the beds are booked already,
There is nothing left for you, sir.
Standing in the rain,
Knocking on the window,
Knocking on the window
On a Christmas Day.
There he is again,
Knocking on the window,
Knocking on the window
In the same old way.

2 No use knocking on the window,
Some are lucky, some are not, sir.
We are Christian men and women,
But we're keeping what we've got, sir.
CHORUS

3 No, we haven't got a manger,
No, we haven't got a stable,
We are Christian men and women,
Ever willing, never able.
CHORUS

4 Christ the Lord has gone to heaven,
One day He'll be coming back, sir.
In this house He will be welcome,
But we hope He won't be black, sir.
CHORUS

5 Wishing you a Merry Christmas,
We will now go back to bed, sir.
'Til you woke us with your knocking,
We were sleeping like the dead, sir.
CHORUS

Reprinted by permission of Essex Music International Ltd

21

A MISTLETOE CAROL

Fred Pratt Green (1903–)   *Traditional Dutch, fifteenth century*

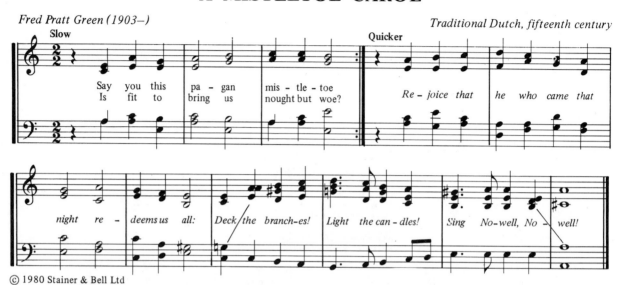

© 1980 Stainer & Bell Ltd

1 Say you this pagan mistletoe
   Is fit to bring us nought but woe?
   Rejoice that he who came that night redeems us all:
   Deck the branches! Light the candles! Sing Nowell, Nowell!

2 Say you these holly berries red
   Are drenched in sacrificial blood?
   CHORUS

3 Say you this Christian holy day
   Was first a pagan holiday?
   CHORUS

4 Say you our Christian joy recalls
   Wild Saturnalian carnivals?
   CHORUS

5 Rejoice that he who came that night
   Turns pagan darkness into light!
   CHORUS

© 1980 Stainer & Bell Limited.

22

FUM, FUM, FUM!

Traditional Spanish
English Version by Bernard A Braley (1924–)

Traditional Spanish

This carol imitates the strumming of guitars ('Fum' = 'Strum'). The opening chords may be played on all the open strings of the guitar from A upwards.

1 The Christmas bells announce a birth.
Fum, Fum, Fum!
The Christ to be is come to earth.
Fum, Fum, Fum!
So dance and feast and sing to celebrate your holy joy:
Today is born for all the world
The promised servant boy.
Fum, Fum, Fum!

2 The Christmas bells announce a birth.
Fum, Fum, Fum!
The Christ to be is come to earth.
Fum, Fum, Fum!
The nature of the God of all revealed in human face
Is come today for all the world
To save our human race.
Fum, Fum, Fum!

23

LONGFELLOW'S CAROL

Henry Wadsworth Longfellow (1807– 1882)

Allen Percival (1925–)

Very steady

I heard the bells on Christmas Day Their old fa-mi - liar ca-rols play, And mild and sweet the words re-peat Of peace on earth, good will to men.

Last time

1 I heard the bells on Christmas Day,
Their old familiar carols play,
And mild and sweet the words repeat
Of peace on earth, good will to men.

2 And thought how, as the day had come,
The belfries of all Christendom
Had rolled along the unbroken song
Of peace on earth, good will to men.

3 Till, ringing, singing on its way,
The world revolved from night to day,
A voice, a chime, a chant sublime
Of peace on earth, good will to men.

4 Then from each black accursed mouth
The cannon thundered in the South,
And with the sound the carols drowned
Of peace on earth, good will to men.

5 It was as if an earthquake rent
The hearth-stones of a continent,
And made forlorn the households born
Of peace on earth, good will to men.

6 And in despair I bowed my head;
'There is no peace on earth,' I said;
'For hate is strong, and mocks the song
Of peace on earth, good will to men.'

7 Then pealed the bells more loud and deep:
'God is not dead; nor doth he sleep!
The wrong shall fail, the right prevail,
With peace on earth, good will to men.'

24

THE WASSAIL OF FIGGY DUFF

*Traditional Words and Music
invented by Michael Flanders (1922–1975)*

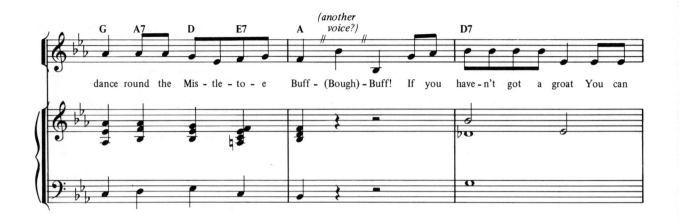

dance round the Mis - tle - to - e Buff - (Bough) - Buff! If you have-n't got a groat You can

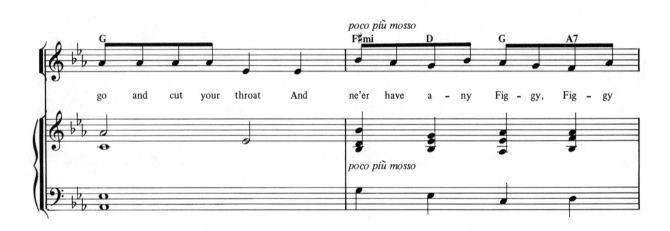

go and cut your throat And ne'er have a - ny Fig-gy, Fig - gy

poco più mosso

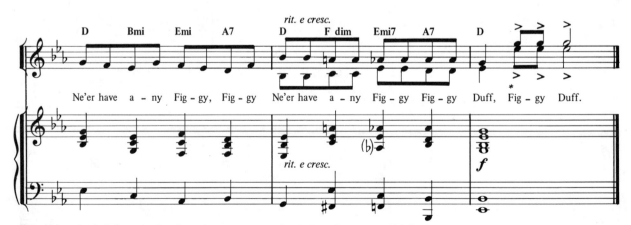

Ne'er have a - ny Fig-gy, Fig-gy Ne'er have a - ny Fig - gy Fig - gy Duff, Fig - gy Duff.

rit. e cresc.

* Each time this 'echo' may be 8vo alt. or 8vo basso or even 15mo alt. or 15mo basso if there are such prodigies in the choir.

52

25

TERLY TERLOW

Anonymous English

Gustav Holst (1874–1934)

blow.

blow.

blow.

blow.

A - bout the field they

A - bout the field they

A - bout the field they

A -

piped full right,_____ It was the mid – dle of the night._____

piped full right,_____ It was the mid – dle of the night:_____

piped full right,_____ It was the mid – dle of the night:_____

cresc.
– bout the field they piped full right, It was the mid – dle of the night:_____

_____ A – down from heav'n there came a light._____ Ter – ly ter – low_____

p

_____ A – down from heav'n there came a light._____ Ter – ly

p

_____ A – down from heav'n there came a light._____

_____ A – down from heav'n there came a light. Ter – ly ter – low_____

p

p

Ter - ly ter - low_____ An - gels_____ there came a

ter - low_____ Ter - ly ter - low_____ An - gels_____ there came a

Ter - ly ter - low_____ Ter - ly_____ An - gels_____ there came a

_____ Ter - ly ter - low_____ An - gels_____ there came a

com-pa-ny, With mer-ry songs and mel - o - dy. The shep - herds a - non_____

com-pa-ny, With mer-ry songs and mel - o - dy. The shep - herds a - non_____

com-pa-ny, With mer-ry songs and mel - o - dy. The shep - herds a - non_____

com-pa-ny, With mer-ry songs and mel - o - dy. The shep - herds a - non_____

gan them as - py._____ Ter - ly ter - low___ The__shepherds

gan them as - py._____ The__ shep - herds

gan them as - py._____ Ter - ly ter - low___ The shepherds

gan them as - py._____ The shep - herds

__ hied them to Beth - le - hem To see that Blessed Son - né - beam,

hied them to Beth - le - hem To see that Bless-ed Son - né - beam,

_ hied them to Beth - le - hem To see that Blessed Son - né - beam,

hied them to Beth - le - hem To see that Bless-ed Son - né - beam, And

59

Child And to His moth-er fair and mild, Whose maid-en - hood was ne'er de -

Ah!_____

Ah!_____

Ah!_____

- filed. Ter - ly ter - low_____ Ter - ly ter - low_____ Ter - ly

Ter - ly ter - low_____ Ter - ly ter - low_____ Ter - ly

Ter - ly ter - low_____ Ter - ly ter - low_____ Ter - ly ter - low_____ de-

Ter - ly ter - low_____ Ter - ly ter - low_____ Ter - ly ter - low_____

pp

The accompaniment was written for oboe and cello but the carol has been sung with keyboard and/or other instruments ever since it was published.

26

TOMORROW SHALL BE MY DANCING DAY

Anonymous

Traditional English

To - mor - row shall be ____ my danc - ing day; I would ____ my

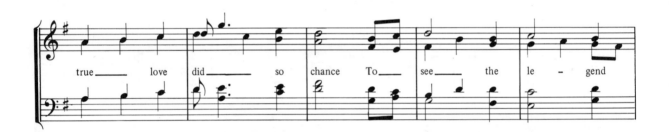

true ____ love did ____ so chance To ____ see the le - gend

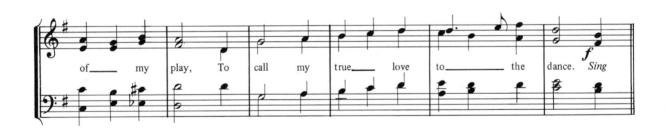

of ____ my play, To call my true ____ love to ____ the dance. Sing

oh! ____ my ____ love, ____ Oh! ____ my love, my love, my love, sing oh! ____ This ____

sing oh! ____ my ____ love ____ love; this

62

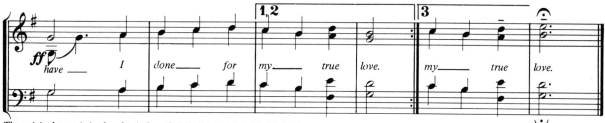

The original tune is in the alto in bars 3 & 4, 7 & 8, 15 & 16, 25 & 26.

1 Tomorrow shall be my dancing day;
  I would my true love did so chance
  To see the legend of my play,
  To call my true love to the dance.
  Sing oh! my love,
  Oh! my love, my love, my love;
  This have I done for my true love.

2 Then was I born of a virgin pure,
  Of her I took my fleshly substance;
  Thus was I knit to Man's nature,
  To call my true love to the dance.
  CHORUS

3 In a manger laid and wrapped I was,
  So very poor, this was my chance,
  Betwixt an ox and a silly poor ass,
  To call my true love to the dance.
  CHORUS

63

27

OUT OF THE ORIENT

Anonymous, sixteenth century

William Byrd (?1542–1623)
Arranged by Thurston Dart (1921–1971)

Out of the o-ri-ent cry-stal skies A blaz-ing star did shine,
Born of a maid of roy-al blood, Who Ma-ry hight by name,

Out of the o-ri-ent cry-stal skies,
Born of a maid of roy-al blood,

Show - ing the Place___ where___ poor - ly lies A
A sa - cred rose,___ which___ once did bud By

A blaz - ing star did shine,   Show - ing the place where___
Who Ma - ry hight by name,   A sa - cred rose, which___

bless - èd Babe di - vine,
grace___ of___ heav'n - ly flame.

poor - ly lies A bless - èd___ Babe di - vine,
once did bud By grace___ of___ heav'n - ly flame.

This shi - ning star three kings___ did

This shi - ning star___ three

65

- to the earth, Where born_____ is this new

peace___ un – to the earth, Where___ born is this new_____

King.

King.

The shep – herds dwell – ing there___ a –

The shep – herds dwell – ing there___ a – bout, the shep – herds

-bout, When they this news did know,

dwell - ing there___ a - bout, When they this news did

Came sing - ing all, e'en in a rout, Fa -

know, Came sing - ing all, came sing - ing___ all,___ e'en in a

-lan - te-ding-di - doe, fa - lan - te-ding-di - doe, fa -

rout, Fa - lan - te-ding-di - doe, fa - lan - te-ding-di -

-lan - te-ding-di-doe, fa - lan-te-ding - di - doe!

-doe, fa - lan - te-ding-di-doe, fa - lan-te-ding-di - doe!

This carol has been transposed up a tone from the original setting for soprano and four viols in British Museum, MSS Egerton 2009-12 and Add. 29401-5, and Harvard, Houghton Library MSS Mus. 30. An optional alto part was added by the editor, together with some suggested dynamics. Spellings have been modernised, and the viol parts adapted for keyboard.

28

THERE IS NO ROSE

English, early fifteenth century

Anonymous c. 1420

The original manuscript is in two parts only in C. The middle part in the chorus is added in accordance with the practice of the time. The carol may be sung a tone lower by SAT as in the transcription by John Stevens © 1963 Stainer & Bell Ltd

There is no rose of such virtue
As is the rose that bare Jesu.

1 There is no rose of such virtue
  As is the rose that bare Jesu;
  Alleluia.
  CHORUS

2 For in this rose contained was
  Heaven and earth in little space;
  Res miranda.
  CHORUS

3 By that rose we may well see
  That he is God in persons three,
  Pari forma.
  CHORUS

4 The angels sungen the shepherds to:
  Gloria in excelsis Deo:
  Gaudeamus.
  CHORUS

5 Leave we all this worldly mirth,
  And follow we this joyful birth;
  Transeamus.
  CHORUS

NOTES: Res miranda = A marvellous thing
     Pari forma   = Of equal form
     Gaudeamus = Let us rejoice
     Transeamus = Let us cross over [from earth to heaven]

29

ROCK THE CRADLE

Trude Bedford (1912–)

Trude Bedford (1912–)

Solo

Rock the cra-dle, rock with gen-tle
Kneel be-fore Him, babe of low es-

S A

pp
Hum throughout (until Coda)

T B

care, Rock the cra-dle, Son of God lies there:
-tate; Kneel and wor-ship

close to hea-ven's gate.

Sing as many of the parts as possible.

Son of God lies there.

© 1980 Stainer & Bell Ltd

1 Rock the cradle, rock with gentle care,
   Rock the cradle, Son of God lies there:
   Kneel before Him, babe of low estate;
   Kneel and worship close to heaven's gate.

2 Rock the cradle, wake not from his rest,
   Rock the cradle, be his watchful guest,
   Kneel before Him—tiny, uncrowned King,
   Kneel and worship, gifts of love to bring.

3 Rock the cradle, nails those hands will tear,
   Rock the cradle, thorns that head must bear;
   Kneel before Him, arms hang for our sake,
   Kneel and worship, heart that men will break.

4 He is sleeping, make no stir or sound,
   Tread there softly—this is holy ground,
   Rock the cradle, rock with gentle care,
   Rock the cradle, Son of God lies there.
   Son of God lies there.

30

GOD REST YOU MERRY, GENTLEMEN

Traditional English ballad, probably seventeenth century

*Traditional English
collected by E F Rimbault (1846)*

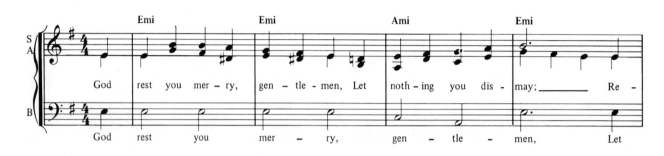

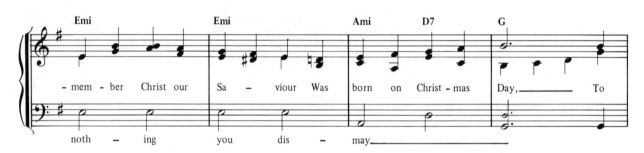

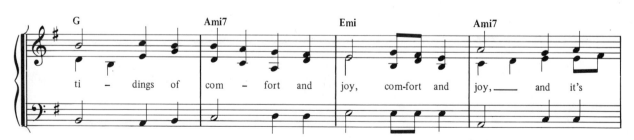

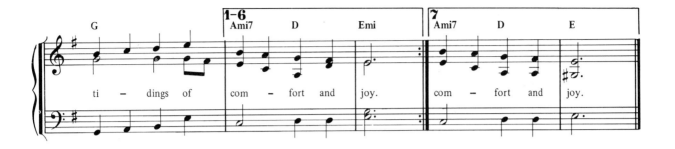

1 God rest you merry, gentlemen,
  Let nothing you dismay;
  Remember Christ our Saviour
  Was born on Christmas Day,
  To save poor souls from Satan's power
  Who long had gone astray,
  And it's tidings of comfort and joy.

2 From God that is our Father
  The blessèd angels came,
  Unto some certain shepherds
  With tidings of the same,
  That there was born in Bethlehem
  The Son of God by name,
  And it's tidings of comfort and joy.

3 'Go, fear not,' said God's angels,
  'Let nothing you affright,
  For there is born in Bethlehem
  Of a pure Virgin bright,
  One able to advance you
  And throw down Satan quite.'
  And it's tidings of comfort and joy.

4 The shepherds at those tidings
  Rejoicèd much in mind,
  And left their flocks a-feeding
  In tempest storms of wind,
  And straight they came to Bethlehem,
  The Son of God to find.
  And it's tidings of comfort and joy.

5 Now when they came to Bethlehem
  Where our sweet Saviour lay,
  They found Him in a manger
  Where oxen feed on hay;
  The blessèd Virgin kneeling down,
  Unto the Lord did pray.
  And it's tidings of comfort and joy.

6 Now to the Lord sing praises,
  All you within this place,
  And with true love and brotherhood
  Each other now embrace;
  This holy tide of Christmas
  All other doth deface.
  And it's tidings of comfort and joy.

Optional instruments (or descant for last verse).

Sing his prai — ses, you with - in this place, love and broth - er - hood now em - brace; This ho - ly tide____ this ho - ly tide all____ oth - er doth____ de - face. And____ it's ti - dings of com-fort and joy.

This carol may be sung in unison with keyboard or with guitar. Unaccompanied verses may be sung (with optional instrumental line if preferred) by SA or SAB groups. SAT groups can put the bass up an octave.

31

GOD'S OWN SON (INFANT IN THE STALL)

Unknown Swiss
English version by Fred Pratt Green (1903–)

Allen Percival (1925–), based on
a German seventeenth century melody

1 O Child, most truly God's own Son,
O crib, O throne of Solomon,
O stall, O place of pure delight,
O straw, like roses red and white!
Infant in the stall, all our sins destroy!
Infant in the straw, give us joy!

2 O Child, most wonderful your Birth,
Your gracious coming to our earth!
Milk-white, blood-red, your body gives
Fresh courage to our humble lives.
CHORUS

3 Your hair is curly, gold your head,
Your eyes are clear, your lips are red,
Most beautiful, most honey sweet
Your body is from head to feet.
CHORUS

4 Like ivory your snow-white skin,
A glowing sapphire set therein:
The sapphire is the Godhead great,
The ivory your mortal state.
CHORUS

5 Your hands are full of summer flowers
That smell more sweetly after showers;
You sparkle, Child, more beautiful
Than if the sun were in the stall.
CHORUS

6 The Godhead lies within your breast
To grant the heart its chief request;
Heav'n has itself no greater grace
Than clearly shines in your sweet face.
CHORUS

Optional voices or instruments

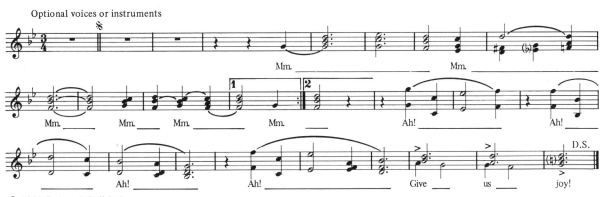

This carol may be sung in unison throughout, but for some choruses the upper stave note may be sung by SSA or SAT, with the lower played on the keyboard or sung by basses in the same rhythm as the upper. The optional line may be sung by male or female groups or played on any 'treble clef' instruments. The B natural in the last bar is only used at the end of the carol.

32

WASSAIL SONG

Traditional Yorkshire
Arranged by R Vaughan Williams (1872–1958)

Anonymous

bless you and send you a hap-py New_ Year._

The humming chorus may be played on keyboard. Guitar chords are only for use as a folk carol with solo voice.

1 We've been awhile a-wandering
  Amongst the leaves so green,
  But now we've come a-wassailing,
  So plainly to be seen:

For it's Christmas time when we travel far and near,
May God bless you and send you a happy New Year.

2 We are not daily beggars
  That beg from door to door,
  But we are neighbours' children
  Whom you have seen before:
  CHORUS

3 We've got a little purse
  Made of stretching leather skin;
  We want a little money
  To line it well within:
  CHORUS

4 Call up the butler of this house,
  Put on his golden ring;
  Let him bring us up a glass of beer,
  And better shall we sing:
  CHORUS

5 So bring us out a table,
  And spread it with a cloth;
  And bring us out a mouldy cheese,
  And then your Christmas loaf:
  CHORUS

6 Good Master and good Mistress,
  While you're sitting by the fire,
  Pray think of us poor children
  That's wandered in the mire:
  CHORUS

33
SONG AND DANCE

Michael Hewlett (1916–)

Traditional Northumbrian,
adapted by John Maynard (1925–)

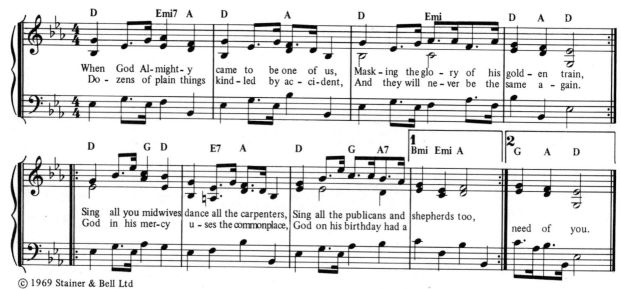

© 1969 Stainer & Bell Ltd

When using guitar chords, place capo on first fret or transpose tune down a semitone.

1 When God Almighty came to be one of us,
Masking the glory of his golden train,
Dozens of plain things kindled by accident,
And they will never be the same again.
Sing all you midwives, dance all the carpenters,
Sing all the publicans and shepherds too,
God in his mercy uses the commonplace,
God on his birthday had a need of you.

2 Splendour of Rome and Local Authority,
Working on policy with furrowed head,
Joined to locate Messiah's nativity,
Just where the prophets had already said.
Sing all you tax-men, dance the Commissioners,
Sing civil servants and policemen too,
God in his purpose uses the governments,
God on his birthday had a need of you.

3 Wise men, they called them, earnest astrologers,
Watching for meaning in the moving stars,
Science or fancy, learned or laughable,
Theirs was a vision that was brought to pass.
Sing all you wise men, dance all the scientists,
Whether your theories are false or true,
God uses knowledge, God uses ignorance,
God on his birthday had a need of you.

4 Sing all creation, made for his purposes,
Called by his providence to live and move:
None is unwanted, none insignificant,
Love needs a universe of folk to love.
Old men and maidens, young men and children,
Black ones and coloured ones and white ones too,
God on his birthday, and to eternity,
God took upon himself the need of you.

© 1969 Stainer & Bell Ltd

82

34

LOCKED IN THE ATOM

Albert Bayly (1901–)

A Ian Sharp (1943–)

© 1980 Stainer & Bell Ltd

1 Locked in the atom God has stored a secret might,
  Energy unmeasured hidden deep from human sight;
  Gift of God for blessing, made by man the tool of fear;
  Shall it evermore be so?

2 Cradled with cattle lay an infant weak and small
  Born of humble peasant, with no dwelling but a stall,
  Yet that heart was pulsing with the Love that made the stars:
  Is it Love with Power too?

3 God, who in lowliness does manifest your power,
  Shewing forth your majesty in atom, star and flower;
  Glory to your greatness! We have seen your love and might,
  Perfected in Bethlehem's child.

Reprinted by permission of the author.

35

DING DONG! MERRILY ON HIGH

G R Woodward (1848–1934)　　　　　　　　　　　　　　　　　　　　*Traditional French*

This carol may be sung in unison with keyboard or with guitar. Groups of SAB and SATB sing as written unaccompanied.

1 Ding dong! Merrily on high
　In heav'n the bells are ringing:
　Ding dong! Verily the sky
　Is riv'n with angels singing.
　Gloria, Hosanna in excelsis!

2 E'en so here below, below,
　Let steeple bells be swungen,
　And i-o, i-o, i-o,
　By priest and people sungen.
　Gloria, Hosanna in excelsis!

3 Pray you, dutifully prime
　Your matin chime, ye ringers;
　May you beautifully rime
　Your evetime song, ye singers.
　Gloria, Hosanna in excelsis!

36

SILENT NIGHT

Joseph Mohr (1792–1848)
English version anonymous

Franz Grüber (1787–1863)

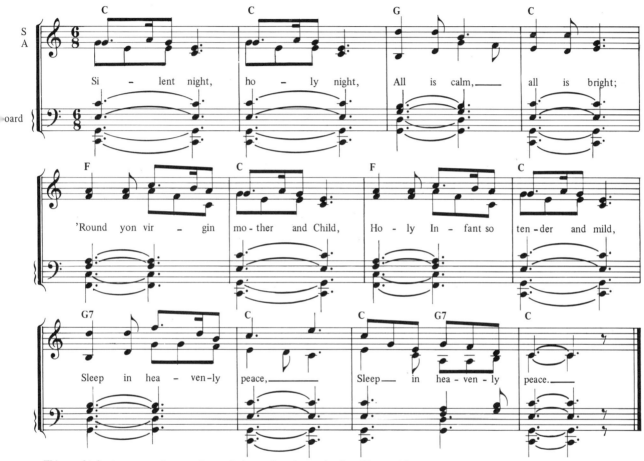

This carol is best sung — as it was written— by two solo voices and guitar. If you wish to sustain another accompaniment, play the bass clef part on a keyboard instrument, using both hands as indicated by the note stems.

1 Silent night, holy night,
  All is calm, all is bright;
  'Round yon virgin mother and Child,
  Holy Infant so tender and mild,
  Sleep in heavenly peace,
  Sleep in heavenly peace.

2 Silent night, holy night,
  Shepherds quake at the sight;
  Glories stream from heaven afar,
  Heav'nly hosts sing Alleluia!
  Christ the Saviour is born!
  Christ the Saviour is born!

3 Silent night, holy night,
  Son of God, love's pure light;
  Radiance beams from thy holy face,
  With the dawn of redeeming grace,
  Jesus, Lord, at thy birth,
  Jesus, Lord, at thy birth.

1 Stille Nacht, heilige Nacht,
  Alles schläft, einsam wacht,
  Nur das traute, hochheilige Paar
  Holder Knabe in lockigen Haar
  Schlafe in himlicher Ruh,
  Schlafe in himlicher Ruh.

2 Stille Nacht, heilige Nacht,
  Hirten erst Kundgemacht,
  Durch der Engel Halleluja
  Tänt es laut von fern und nah,
  Christ der Retter ist da
  Christ der Retter ist da.

3 Stille Nacht, heilige Nacht,
  Gottes Sohn o wie lacht
  Lieb aus deinem Göttlichen Mund,
  Da uns schlägt die rettende Stund.
  Christ in deiner Geburt,
  Christ in deiner Geburt.

37

CAROL FOR CHRISTINGLE

NOTE: At Christmas, the Moravian Church in Czechoslovakia holds a service for children known as the 'Christingle Service'. After the singing of carols and the telling of the Christmas story, trays of oranges, decorated with four feathers, sweets, and a lighted candle, are brought into the church. Each child receives an orange, to be taken home. This carol explains the symbolism. Christingle services are now widely held in Britain and other countries.

Fred Pratt Green (1903–)   *Traditional Czech*

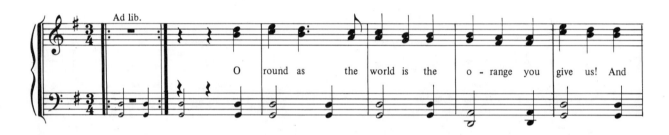

O round as the world is the o-range you give us! And

hap-py are they who to Je-sus be-long: So let the world know, as we

join in Christ-in-gle, That Je-sus, the Hope of the World, is our song.

© 1980 Stainer & Bell Ltd

* Repeat the 'drone' as many times as you wish, becoming softer and slower until the end. If guitar is used, play left hand notes only, an octave higher (not chords) throughout. Cellists should use open strings for G and D, and double-stop for D and A; violas may play the left hand 'drone' an octave higher in the same way.

1 O round as the world is the orange you give us!
And happy are they who to Jesus belong:
So let the world know, as we join in Christingle,
That Jesus, the Hope of the World, is our song.

2 O bright is the flame of the candle you give us!
And happy are they who to Jesus belong:
So let the world know, as we join in Christingle,
That Jesus, the Light of the World, is our song.

3 Go northward or southward, go eastward or westward,
How happy are they who to Jesus belong:
So let the world know, as we join in Christingle,
That Jesus, the Peace of the World, is our song.

4 When homeward we go, we must take Jesus with us,
For happy are we who to Jesus belong;
So let the world know, as we join in Christingle,
That Jesus, the Saviour of All, is our Song.

38

NOWELL, SING WE

Mediaeval English *Mediaeval English*

No - well sing we ___ now all ___ and ___ some, For rex pa-

-ci - fi - cus ___ is ___ come. In Beth' - lem in ___ that ___

fair ci - ty, A child was born of ___ a mai -

-den ___ free, That shall a lord and prin - cë be,

Originally for ATT, this carol may be sung by TBarB transposing down a fourth. Alternatively two voices only sing the top stave with an instrument playing the alto and a drum repeating the rhythm throughout.

Nowell sing we now all and some,
For rex pacificus is come.

1 In Beth'lem in that fair city,
  A child was born of a maiden free,
  That shall a lord and princë be,
  A solis ortus cardine.
  CHORUS

2 Children were slain full great plenty,
  Jesu, for the love of thee;
  Wherefore their soulës saved be,
  Hostis Herodis impie.
  CHORUS

3 As sunnë shineth though the glass,
  So Jesu in his mother was;
  Thee to servë now grant us grace,
  O lux beata Trinitas.
  CHORUS

4 Now God is comën to worshipën us;
  Now of Mary is born Jesus;
  Make we merry amongës us;
  Exultet celum laudibus.
  CHORUS

NOTES: Rex pacificus = King of Peace
      A solis ortus cardine = From the point of the rising sun
      Hostis Herodis impie = The enemy, Herod the ungodly
      O lux beata Trinitas = O Light, Blessed Trinity
      Exultet celum* laudibus = Let the sky sing out with praise

* pronounced 'shaylum'

39

TYROLEAN CRADLE SONG

Thomas Armstrong (1898—) Traditional Tyrolean

The sha – dows are fal – ling, the even-ing's at hand,
To watch by thy cra – dle, my Sa – viour, I stand: A song I am

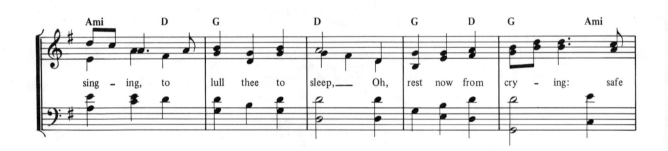

sing – ing, to lull thee to sleep,___ Oh, rest now from cry – ing: safe

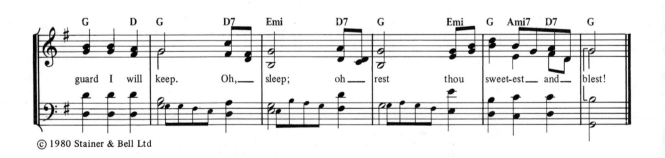

guard I will keep. Oh,___ sleep; oh___ rest thou sweet-est___ and___ blest!

This carol may be sung in unison with keyboard (playing small notes) or with guitar. It may also be sung unaccompanied, with or without the optional instrument line, by SA, SAT, SAB, SATB as written. SSA choirs should sing SAT parts, preferably in the key of A.

Optional instruments

1 The shadows are falling, the evening's at hand,
  To watch by thy cradle, my Saviour, I stand:
  A song I am singing, to lull thee to sleep,
  Oh, rest now from crying: safe guard I will keep.
  Oh, sleep; oh, rest, thou sweetest and blest!

2 Forget for a moment the sorrows of earth,
  Man's burden of sin that thou bearest from birth;
  Forget the poor stable where thou must rest,
  If thou dost accept it, no palace so blest.
  Oh, sleep; oh, rest, thou sweetest and blest!

3 Thy glory gives grace to the manger and stall,
  On me at thy side may a benison fall:
  Thus blest with thy presence, 'tis here I would be,
  Child Jesus, my Saviour, ne'er parted from thee.
  Oh, sleep; oh, rest, thou sweetest and blest!

40

RESONET IN LAUDIBUS
(COME WITH ALL BELIEVERS TRUE)

Latin in Piae Cantiones, 1582
English Version by Bernard A Braley (1924—)

Melody as in Piae Cantiones, 1582

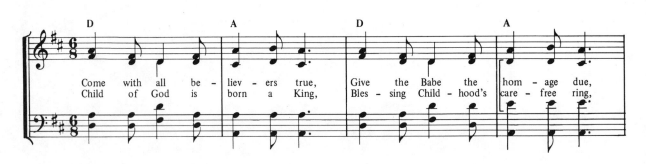

Come with all be - liev - ers true, Give the Babe the hom - age due,
Child of God is born a King, Bles - sing Child - hood's care - free ring,

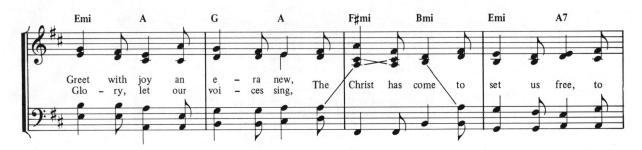

Greet with joy an e - ra new, The Christ has come to set us free, to
Glo - ry, let our voi - ces sing,

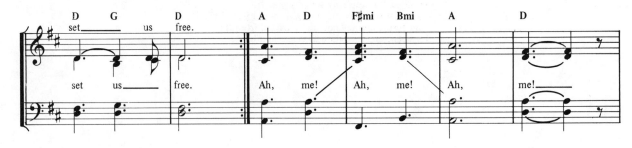

set us free.
set us free. Ah, me! Ah, me! Ah, me!

Vir - gin Moth - er bears God's gift, Planned by God our hopes to lift, Praise be! Praise

be!_____ An—swer born to sin's deep rift In Is—ra—el

Tru—ly told by Ga—————bri—el.

This carol may be sung in unison with keyboard or solo with guitar. SA, SAB, SATB choirs may sing verses unaccompanied as written.

Resonet in laudibus
Cum jucundis plausibus
Sion cum fidelibus;
Apparuit quem genuit Maria!
Omnes nunc concinite,
Nato regi psallite
Voce pia dicite:
Sit gloria Christo nostro Infantia!
Eia, Eia, Eia!
Virgo deum paruit
Quem divina voluit potentia.
Hodie apparuit in Israel,
Quem praedixit Gabriel.

Come with all believers true,
Give the Babe the homage due,
Greet with joy an era new,
The Christ has come to set us free, to set us free.
Child of God is born a King,
Blessing Childhood's carefree ring,
Glory, let our voices sing,
The Christ has come to set us free, to set us free.
Ah, me! Ah, me! Ah, me!
Virgin Mother bears God's gift,
Planned by God our hopes to lift,
Praise be! Praise be!
Answer born to sin's deep rift
In Israel
Truly told by Gabriel.

41

REJOICE AND BE MERRY

Traditional Dorset, probably 18th century

Traditional English West Country

Re - joice and be_ mer - ry in songs and in mirth!_ O praise our Re -
-deem - er, all mor - tals on earth! For_ this is the birth - day of
Je - sus our King,_ Who_ brought us sal - va - tion; his_ prai - ses we'll sing!

This carol may be sung unaccompanied or with keyboard or guitar.

Optional instruments (preferably brass or reed)

Repeat from ℅ if 'First
Nowell' descant is being
sung.

1 Rejoice and be merry in songs and in mirth!
  O praise our Redeemer, all mortals on earth!
  For this is the birthday of Jesus our King,
  Who brought us salvation; his praises we'll sing.

2 A heavenly vision appeared in the sky;
  Vast numbers of angels the shepherds did spy,
  Proclaiming the birthday of Jesus our King,
  Who brought us salvation; his praises we'll sing.

3 Likewise a bright star in the sky did appear,
  Which led the wise men from the east to draw near;
  They found the Messiah, sweet Jesus our King,
  Who brought us salvation; his praises we'll sing.

4 And when they were come, they their treasures unfold,
  And unto him offered myrrh, incense, and gold.
  So blessed for ever be Jesus our King,
  Who brought us salvation; his praises we'll sing.

It has been suggested that the tune of 'The First Nowell' may have begun its life as a descant to this carol. Choirs who wish may sing the first verse of 'The First Nowell' (to the tune as printed below) with the first verse of 'Rejoice and Be Merry' sung again (repeating the last two lines of the latter), to end the carol.

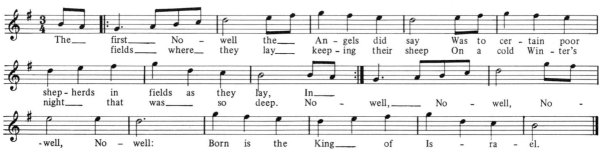

42
THE FIRST NOWELL

Optional instruments (preferably brass or reed)

1 The first Nowell the angel did say
   Was to certain poor shepherds in fields as they lay;
   In fields where they lay keeping their sheep,
   On a cold winter's night that was so deep.
   Nowell, Nowell, Nowell, Nowell,
   Born is the King of Israel.

2 They lookëd up and saw a star
   Shining in the east, beyond them far,
   And to the earth it gave great light,
   And so it continued both day and night.
   CHORUS

3 And by the light of that same star,
   Three wise men came from country far;
   To seek for a King was their intent,
   And to follow the star wherever it went.
   CHORUS

4 This star drew nigh to the north-west;
   O'er Bethlehem it took its rest,
   And there it did both stop and stay
   Right over the place where Jesus lay.
   CHORUS

5 Then entered in those wise men three
   Full reverently upon their knee,
   And offered there in His presence
   Their gold, and myrrh, and frankincense.
   CHORUS

6 Then let us all with one accord
   Sing praises to our heavenly Lord,
   That hath made heaven and earth of nought,
   And with His blood mankind hath bought.
   CHORUS

43

WIND THROUGH THE OLIVE TREES

Traditional American   *Traditional American*

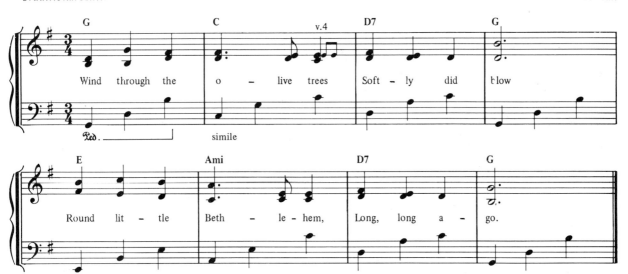

Wind through the olive trees Softly did blow Round little Bethlehem, Long, long ago.

Round little Bethlehem, Long, long ago.

This carol is for unison or solo with keyboard or with guitar. Unaccompanied verses may be sung by taking the top two parts of the right hand.

1 Wind through the olive trees
  Softly did blow
  Round little Bethlehem,
  Long, long ago.

2 Sheep on the hillside lay
  Whiter than snow,
  Shepherds were watching them,
  Long, long ago.

3 Then from the starry skies
  Angels bent low
  Singing their songs of joy,
  Long, long ago.

4 Wise men were following
  A star that did glow
  Far over Bethlehem,
  Long, long ago.

44

SONG TO THE CHRISTMAS TREE

Norwegian words by Johan Krohn
English version by Bernard Braley (1924–)
from a translation by Turid Bakke.

Edvard Grieg (1843–1907)

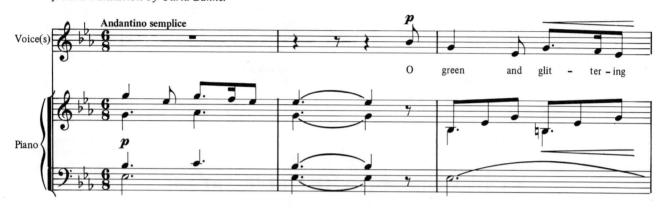

O green and glit - ter - ing

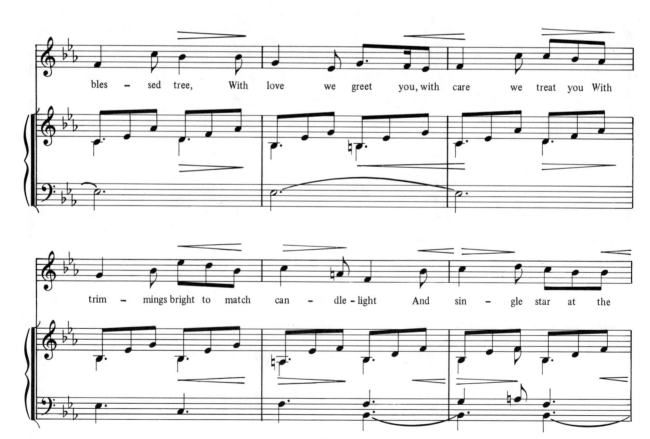

bles - sed tree, With love we greet you, with care we treat you With

trim - mings bright to match can - dle - light And sin - gle star at the

1 O green and glittering blessed tree,
With love we greet you, with care we treat you
With trimmings bright to match candlelight
And single star at the topmost swaying,
The news relaying—what God is saying
At Christmas time.

2 O bright and glistering blessed star,
By your soft glowing, so God was showing,
As angels smiled upon holy Child,
A gift had come of the topmost breeding,
A lowly pleading for human reading,
The Word made Flesh.

3 O true and catholic blessed tale,
My mother told me, how Christ would hold me—
O tree so bright, may your Christmas light
Tell every person the revelation
Of God's salvation for every nation
The Gospel true.

45

ANGELS FROM THE REALMS OF GLORY

J Montgomery (1771–1854)   *Traditional French*

An - gels, from the___ realms of glo - ry, Wing your___ flight o'er___ all the earth;
Ye who sang cre - a - tion's sto - ry Now pro - claim Mes - si - ah's birth:

Come___ and___ wor - ship
Come___ O___ come, ___ O___ come ___ and ___ wor - ship___
Come___ and wor - ship ___

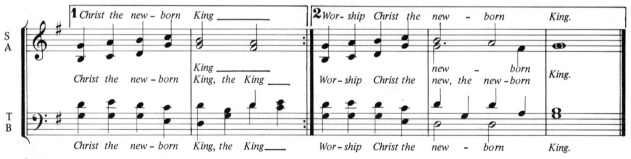

1 Christ the new - born King ___
Christ the new - born King, the King ___
Christ the new - born King, the King___

2 Wor - ship Christ the new - born King.
new - born King.
Wor - ship Christ the new, the new - born King.
Wor - ship Christ the new - born King.

This carol may be sung in unison with keyboard or by SA, SAB, SATB choirs accompanied or unaccompanied.

1 Angels, from the realms of glory,
  Wing your flight o'er all the earth;
  Ye who sang creation's story
  Now proclaim Messiah's birth:
  Come and worship,
  Worship Christ the new-born King.

2 Shepherds in the field abiding,
  Watching o'er your flocks by night,
  God with man is now residing;
  Yonder shines the infant Light:
  CHORUS

3 Sages, leave your contemplations;
  Brighter visions beam afar;
  Seek the great Desire of Nations;
  Ye have seen his natal star:
  CHORUS

4 Saints before the altar bending,
  Watching long in hope and fear,
  Suddenly the Lord, descending,
  In his temple shall appear:
  CHORUS

5 Though an infant now we view him,
  He shall fill his Father's throne,
  Gather all the nations to him;
  Every knee shall then bow down:
  CHORUS

46

O CHRISTMAS TREE

English version by Bernard A Braley (1924–)

Traditional German, 19th century

O Christ-mas tree, O Christ-mas tree, the tree for ev – ery sea – son, Your

dress of green on sum-mer morn Is trimmed in white by win-ter storm. O

Christ – mas tree, O Christ – mas tree, the tree for ev – ery sea – son.

This carol may be sung in unison or solo with piano or with guitar. SA, SAB, SAT, and SATB choirs may sing verses or choruses unaccompanied to vary the texture. SSA groups sing the right-hand parts with the bass an octave up.

Optional instruments or equal voice backing for use with solo voice only.

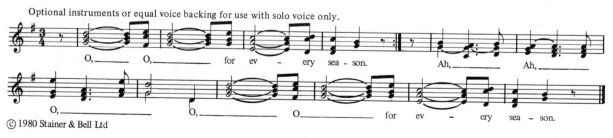

O, _____ O, _____ for ev – ery sea – son. Ah, _____ Ah, _____

O, _____ O, _____ O _____ for ev – ery sea – son.

1 *O Christmas tree, O Christmas tree, the tree for every season,*
O Christmas tree, O Christmas tree, the tree for every season,
Your dress of green on summer morn
Is trimmed in white by winter storm.
O Christmas tree, O Christmas tree, the tree for every season.

2 *CHORUS*
Your star-lit boughs of candles bright
Sing out with joy to our delight,
O Christmas tree, O Christmas tree, the tree for every season.

3 *CHORUS*
Throughout the year, your lively green
Reminds us of the Christ unseen,
O Christmas tree, O Christmas tree, the tree for every season.

4 *CHORUS*
You dress with God-like constancy,
The symbol of eternity,
O Christmas tree, O Christmas tree, the tree for every season.

47

WE THREE KINGS

J H Hopkins (1820–1891)   *J H Hopkins (1820–1891)*

We three kings of o - ri - ent are; Bear - ing gifts we tra - verse a -

far, Field and foun - tain, moor and moun - tain, Fol - low - ing

yon - der star: O_____ star of won - der, star of

night, Star with roy - al beau - ty bright, West - ward

lead - ing, still pro - ceed - ing, Guide us to thy per - fect light.

This carol may be sung in unison with keyboard or with guitar. SA or SAB sing with or without accompaniment; SSA altos sing the bass an octave higher. The small notes in the tenor may be sung by three men (or three girls), if the carol is dramatised as follows:

1 We three kings of orient are;
  Bearing gifts we traverse afar,
  Field and fountain, moor and mountain,
  Following yonder star:
  O star of wonder, star of night,
  Star with royal beauty bright,
  Westward leading, still proceeding,
  Guide us to thy perfect light.

2 Born a king on Bethlehem plain,
  Gold I bring, to crown him again,
  King for ever, ceasing never,
  Over us all to reign:
  CHORUS

3 Frankincense to offer have I,
  Incense owns a deity nigh;
  Prayer and praising, all men raising,
  Worship him, God most high:
  CHORUS

4 Myrrh is mine; its bitter perfume
  Breathes a life of gathering gloom;
  Sorrowing, sighing, bleeding, dying,
  Sealed in the stone-cold tomb:
  CHORUS

5 Glorious now behold him arise,
  King and God and sacrifice,
  Alleluya, alleluya,
  Earth to the heavens replies:
  CHORUS

All three sing:

1 We three kings from afar
  Following the brightest star:
  O bright star,
  Guide us to thy light.

Melchior sings:

2 Melchior, bringing gold:
  King for ever he shall reign.
  O bright star,
  Guide us to thy light.

Caspar sings:

3 Frankincense, Caspar brings:
  Prayer and praising God most high.
  O bright star,
  Guide us to thy light.

Balthazar sings:

4 Balthazar, bringing myrrh:
  Bitter perfume for the tomb.
  O bright star,
  Guide us to thy light.

All three sing:

5 Gloria now, King and God:
  Alleluya earth replies.
  O bright star,
  Guide us to thy light.

Optional instruments

48

IN DULCI JUBILO

Traditional German/Latin c. 1500
English/Latin translation by
Allen Percival (1925–)

German fifteenth century, harmonised by
R L de Pearsall (1795–1856)

Optional instruments or voices. As this was originally a macaronic or mixed-language carol, voices sing in German and Latin.

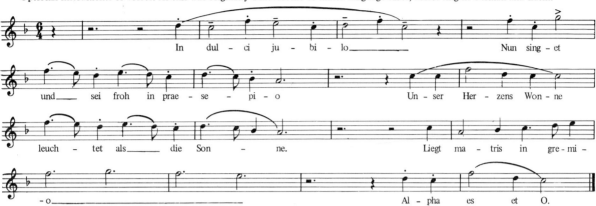

In dul - ci ju - bi - lo _____ Nun sing - et

und ___ sei froh in prae - se - pi - o Un - ser Her - zens Won - ne

leuch - tet als ___ die Son - ne. Liegt ma - tris in gre - mi -

-o _____ Al - pha es et O.

NOTES: In dulci jubilo = In sweet jubilation (pronounce 'dul-shee yoobilo')
In praesepio = In a manger (pronounce 'pray-seppio')
Matris in gremio = In mother's lap (pronounce 'matreece in graymeeo')
Alpha es et O! = (You are) the beginning and the end
Nun singet und sei froh = Now sing and be happy
Unser Herzens Wonne = Our Hearts' Wonder
Leuchtet als die Sonne = Shines like the Sun
Liegt = Lies

49

O LITTLE TOWN OF BETHLEHEM

Phillips Brooks (1835–93)   *Traditional English*

O lit – tle town of Beth – le – hem, How still we see thee lie! A –
-bove thy deep and dream – less sleep The si – lent stars go

by. Yet in thy dark streets shi – neth The e – ver – last – ing

light; The hopes and fears of all the years Are met in thee to - night.

You may like to sing this tune occasionally as a change, composed by Lewis H Redner when the carol was written:

1 O little town of Bethlehem,
   How still we see thee lie!
   Above thy deep and dreamless sleep
   The silent stars go by.
   Yet in thy dark streets shineth
   The everlasting light;
   The hopes and fears of all the years
   Are met in thee tonight.

2 O morning stars together
   Proclaim the holy birth,
   And praises sing to God the King,
   And peace to men on earth;
   For Christ is born of Mary;
   And gathered all above,
   While mortals sleep, the angels keep
   Their watch of wond'ring love.

3 How silently, how silently,
   The wondrous gift is giv'n!
   So God imparts to human hearts
   The blessings of his heav'n.
   No ear may hear his coming;
   But in this world of sin,
   Where meek souls will receive him, still
   The dear Christ enters in.

4 O holy Child of Bethlehem,
   Descend to us, we pray;
   Cast out our sin, and enter in,
   Be born in us today.
   We hear the Christmas angels
   The great glad tidings tell:
   O come to us, abide with us,
   Our Lord Emmanuel.

50

THE MOLE END CAROL

Kenneth Grahame (1859–1932)   *Michael Sanders (1913–)*

1 Vil - la - gers all this
2 Here we stand in the
3 Ere one half of the
4 Good man Jo - seph

fros - ty tide,   Let your doors swing o - pen wide; Though wind may fol - low and
cold and the sleet   Blow - ing fingers and stamp - ing feet   Come from far a - way
night was gone,   Sud - den a star had led us on   Rain - ing bliss and
toiled thro' the snow, Saw the star o'er a sta - ble low,   Ma - ry she might not

snow be - side   Yet draw us in by your fire to bide,   Joy shall be
you to greet,   You by the fire___ and we in the street   Bid - ding you
ben - i - son,   Bliss to - mor - row and more a - non,   Joy for
fur - ther go,   Wel - come thatch___ and lit - ter be - low,   Joy shall be

Guitar chords should be used in arpeggio except for bars 9 and 10, and the last four bars.

111

51

'I' SAID THE DONKEY

Adapted by Christopher Rowe

Traditional West Indian

'I' said the don-key, all shag-gy and brown, 'Car-ried his mo-ther all

in - to the town; Car - ried her up - hill, car - ried her

down, I' said the don - key, all shag - gy and brown.

Reprinted by permission of EFDS Publications Ltd

The words of each verse will vary in rhythm according to natural pronunciation on these basic notes, bar by bar:

1 'I' said the donkey, all shaggy and brown,
   'Carried his mother all into the town;
   Carried her uphill, carried her down,
   I' said the donkey, all shaggy and brown.

2 'I' said the cow, with spots of red,
   'Gave him hay for to rest his head;
   Gave a manger for his bed,
   I' said the cow, with spots of red.

3 'I' said the sheep, with twisted horn,
   'Gave my wool for to keep him warm;
   Gave my coat on Christmas morn,
   I' said the sheep with twisted horn.

4 'I' said the dove from the rafters high,
   'Cooed him to sleep with a lullaby;
   Cooed him to sleep my mate and I,
   I' said the dove from the rafters high.

5 Thus every beast, every bird as well,
   In the stable there was wont to tell;
   Of the gift he gave Emmanuel,
   Of the gift he gave Emmanuel.

Reprinted by permission EFDS Publications Ltd.

Optional Instruments

52
SUSANNI

Traditional German
English version by Marie Chatterley

Traditional German

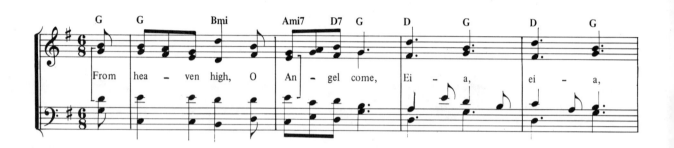

From hea — ven high, O An — gel come, Ei — a, ei — a,

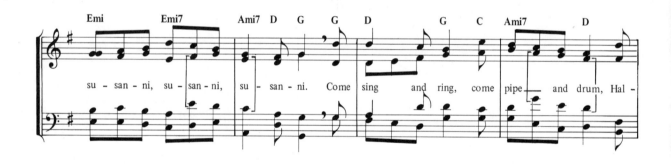

su — san — ni, su — san — ni, su — san — ni. Come sing and ring, come pipe and drum, Hal —

—le — lu — jah! hal — le — lu — jah! Oh, sing of Ma — ry and Je — sus.

This carol may be sung in unison with keyboard or with guitar. Two-part choirs may sing the top two parts with or without accompaniment; SAB or SATB sing as written; SSA altos sing the bass part an octave higher.

Optional instruments

1 Vom Himmel hoch, O Engel, kommt!
  Eia, eia, susanni, susanni, susanni.
  Kommt singt und klingt, kommt pfeif und trombt,
  Hallelujah! hallelujah!.....
  Von Jesus singt und Maria.

2 Kommt ohne instrumenten nicht,
  Eia, eia, susanni, susanni, susanni.
  Bringt lauten, harfen, geigen mit!
  Hallelujah! hallelujah!
  Von Jesus singt und Maria.

3 Lasst hören euer stimmen viel,
  Eia, eia, susanni, susanni, susanni.
  Mit orgel und mit saitenspiel
  Hallelujah! hallelujah!
  Von Jesus singt und Maria.

1 From heaven high, O Angel come,
  Eia, eia, susanni, susanni, susanni.
  Come sing and ring, come pipe and drum,
  Hallelujah! hallelujah!
  Oh, sing of Mary and Jesus.

2 Come tune your instruments with me,
  Eia, eia, susanni, susanni, susanni.
  Bring lutes and harps and violins,
  Hallelujah! hallelujah!
  Oh, sing of Mary and Jesus.

3 O let us hear your voices clear,
  Eia, eia, susanni, susanni, susanni.
  With organ and with psalterie,
  Hallelujah! hallelujah!
  Oh, sing of Mary and Jesus.

NOTE: susanni = hosanna

53

ROCKING CAROL

Traditional Czech
English version by Margaret Tausky (1904–)

Traditional Czech

© 1980 Stainer & Bell Ltd

This carol is best sung unaccompanied or with guitar. If you wish, sustain it with the bass part (played with both hands) on a keyboard instrument ..... softly.

1 Sleep now, Jesus, Baby King,
   We will sing,
   And a coat of fur we'll bring.
   We will rock you, rock you, rock you.
   Safe and warm in sleep we'll lock you,
   Serve and love you all we can,
   Son of God and Son of Man.

2 Sleep now, Jesus, little one,
   Mary's son,
   Children all to you shall run.
   We will rock you, rock you, rock you.
   Safe and warm in sleep we'll lock you,
   By the manger watch we'll keep,
   Little Jesus, sweetly sleep.

Chronicles

54

THE BELL OF CREATION

Sydney Carter (1915–)

Sydney Carter (1915–)

With capo on third fret:

The bell of cre-a-tion is swing-ing for e-ver In all of the things that are com-ing to be, The bell of cre-a-tion is swing-ing for e-ver And all of the while it is swing-ing in me.

Swing, bell, o-ver the land! Swing,

bell, un - der the sea! The bell of cre - a - tion is

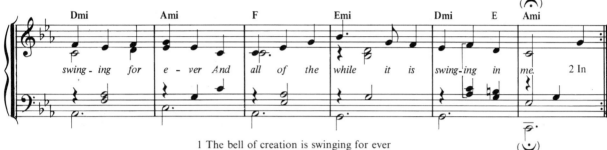

swing - ing for e - ver And all of the while it is swing-ing in me. 2 In

1 The bell of creation is swinging for ever
In all of the things that are coming to be,
The bell of creation is swinging for ever
And all of the while it is swinging in me.
Swing, bell, over the land!
Swing, bell, under the sea!
The bell of creation is swinging for ever
And all of the while it is swinging in me.

2 In all of my loving, in all of my labour,
In all of the things that are coming to be,
In all of my loving, in all of my labour,
The bell of creation is swinging in me.
CHORUS

3 I look for the life that is living for ever
In all of the things that are coming to be,
I look for the life that is living for ever
And all of the while it is looking for me.
CHORUS

4 I'll swing with the bell that is swinging for ever
In all of the things that are coming to be,
I'll swing with the bell that is swinging for ever
And all of the while it is swinging in me.
CHORUS

Optional 'bell-like' instruments, C and G only.

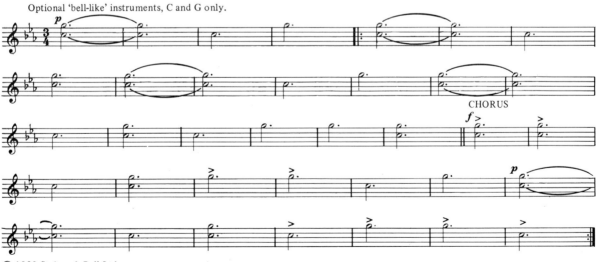

55

THIS IS THE TRUTH

Traditional Herefordshire

Traditional Herefordshire
Harmonised by R Vaughan Williams (1872–1958)

Guitar chords are for use with melody only.

1 This is the truth sent from above,
  The truth of God, the God of love;
  Therefore don't turn me from your door,
  But hearken all both rich and poor.

2 The first thing which I do relate
  Is that God did Man create,
  The next thing which to you I'll tell;
  Woman was made with man to dwell.

3 Then after this 'twas God's own choice
  To place them both in Paradise,
  There to remain from evil free,
  Except they ate of such a tree.

4 And they did eat, which was a sin,
  And thus their ruin did begin,
  Ruined themselves, both you and me,
  And all of their posterity.

5 Thus we were heirs to endless woes
  Till God the Lord did interpose,
  And so a promise soon did run
  That He would redeem us by His Son.

120

56

YOU CALL AND CREATE FROM BLINDNESS AND DEATH

Fred Kaan (1929–) from the Swedish of
Anders Frostenson (1906–)

Lars Åke Lundberg (1935–)

This carol may be sung solo or unison with keyboard and/or with guitar. If the guitar chords in the verse are too difficult, use those in brackets.

All that we have comes from you,
All your love comes true;
All that we have comes from you,
All your love comes true.

1 You call and create from blindness and death the things that are.
Your Word on its way, your Spirit released, renew what is.
CHORUS

2 Your reign comes to light 'mid rubble and dust, a treasure found.
The price of our life: your cross and your grave; with you we rise.
CHORUS

3 Creation is yours, its hurt is our call to rise and serve.
From you we receive the gift we must lay in hungering hands.
CHORUS

English words © 1976 Stainer & Bell Ltd

Translated from the Swedish by permission of the original author.

57
GEORGE FOX (A PROTESTER'S CAROL)

Sydney Carter (1915—)

*Traditional Morris Dance Tune
adapted by Sydney Carter (1915—)*

There's a light that is shin-ing In the

1 heart of a man, There's a light that was shin-ing When the world be-gan.
2 Turk and the Jew And a light that is shin-ing,friend,In me and in you.

Old lea-ther bree-ches, Shag-gy, shag-gy locks! (Old lea-ther bree-ches, Shaggy,shag-gy locks.) With your

old lea-ther breeches And your shag-gy, shag-gy locks You are pul-ling down the pil-lars of the world,George Fox!

Small notes in the right hand part should be omitted when there are instruments or a whistling chorus; otherwise the words should be repeated.

1 There's a light that is shining
  In the heart of a man,
  There's a light that was shining
  When the world began.
  There's a light that is shining
  In the Turk and the Jew
  And a light that is shining, friend,
  In me and in you.
  Old leather breeches,
  Shaggy, shaggy locks!
  (Old leather breeches,
  Shaggy, shaggy locks!)
  With your old leather breeches
  And your shaggy, shaggy locks
  You are pulling down
  The pillars of
  The world, George Fox!

2 With a book and a steeple,
  With a bell and a key
  They would bind it forever
  But they can't (said he).
  Oh, the book it will perish
  And the steeple will fall
  But the light will be shining
  At the end of it all.
  CHORUS

3 'If we give you a pistol,
  Will you fight for the Lord?'
  'But you can't kill the devil
  With a gun or a sword.'
  'Will you swear on the Bible?'
  'I will not,' said he,
  'For the truth is more holy
  Than the book to me.'
  CHORUS

4 There's an ocean of darkness
  And I drown in the night
  Till I come through the darkness
  To the ocean of light,
  You can lock me in prison
  But the light will be free,
  'And I walk in the glory
  Of the light,' said he.
  CHORUS

Optional instruments (or whistlers)

58

JACOB'S LADDER

Traditional, seventeenth century

Traditional English

As Ja - cob with tra - vel was wear - y one day,___ At ___ night on a
stone___ for a pil - low he lay; He___ saw in a vi - sion a lad - der so
high That its foot was on earth,___ and its top in the sky: Al - le -
-lu - ya to Je - sus, who died on the Tree,___ And hath raised up a lad - der of
mer - cy for me, And hath raised up a lad - der of mer - cy for me.

This carol may be sung in unison with keyboard or with guitar. It may also be sung SSA with the written bass up an octave.

1 As Jacob with travel was weary one day,
At night on a stone for a pillow he lay;
He saw in a vision a ladder so high
That its foot was on earth, and its top in the sky:
Alleluya to Jesus, who died on the Tree,
And hath raised up a ladder of mercy for me,
And hath raised up a ladder of mercy for me.

2 This ladder is long, it is strong and well-made,
Has stood hundreds of years and is not yet decayed;
Many millions have climbed it and reached Zion's hill,
And thousands by faith are climbing it still:
CHORUS

3 Come let us ascend! all may climb it who will;
For the angels of Jacob are guarding it still:
And remember each step, that by faith we pass o'er,
Some prophet or martyr hath trod it before:
CHORUS

4 And when we arrive at the haven of rest
We shall hear the glad words, 'Come up hither, ye blest,
Here are regions of light, here are mansions of bliss:'
O, who would not climb such a ladder as this?
CHORUS

Optional instruments for chorus only.

59

COME, LEAVE YOUR WORK

Bernard A Braley (1924–) French Tune 'Quittez Pasteurs'

Come, leave your work, your dai-ly toil and wor-ry, Come, leave the chores, fore-go do-mes-tic care, This is a day for wor-ship and re-joic-ing. The Lord of earth and heaven, The Lord, the Lord of earth and heaven is here, The Lord, the Lord, the Lord, the Lord of earth and heaven is here.

1 Come, leave your work, your daily toil and worry,
  Come, leave the chores, forego domestic care,
  This is a day for worship and rejoicing.
  The Lord of earth and heaven,
  The Lord, the Lord of earth and heaven is here,
  The Lord, the Lord, the Lord, the Lord of earth and heaven
  *   is here.*

2 Come, heal the wounds, the daily wounds of suffering,
  Come, use your life, to stay another's tear.
  CHORUS

3 Come, speak your mind, rebel against injustice,
  Let not your greed deny another's share.
  CHORUS

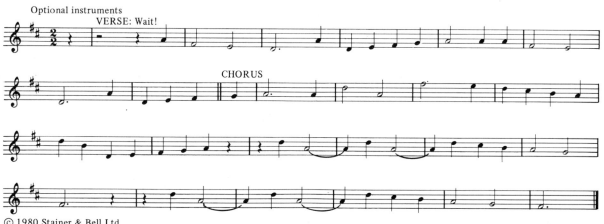

60

CAROL OF THE UNIVERSE

Sydney Carter (1915–)

Sydney Carter (1915–)

1 Every star shall sing a carol:
Every creature, high or low,
Come and praise the King of Heaven
By whatever name you know.
God above, Man below.
Holy is the name I know.

2 When the King of all creation
Had a cradle on the earth,
Holy was the human body,
Holy was the human birth.
CHORUS

3 Who can tell what other cradle
High above the Milky Way
Still may rock the King of Heaven
On another Christmas Day?
CHORUS

4 Who can count how many crosses,
Still to come or long ago.
Crucify the King of Heaven?
Holy is the name I know.
CHORUS

5 Who can tell what other body
He will hallow for his own?
I will praise the Son of Mary.
Brother of my blood and bone.
CHORUS

6 Every star and every planet.
Every creature high and low,
Come and praise the King of Heaven
By whatever name you know.
CHORUS

61

WHICH ONE IS WHICH?

Sydney Carter (1915–)   *Sydney Carter (1915–)*

1 I come like a beggar
With a gift in my hand;
I come like a beggar
With a gift in my hand.
By the hungry I will feed you,
By the poor I make you rich,
By the broken I will mend you.
Tell me,
Which one is which?

2 I come like a prisoner
To bring you the key,
I come like a prisoner
To bring you the key:
CHORUS

3 By the need of another,
By the gift that I bring;
By the need of another,
By the gift that I bring.
CHORUS

Optional descant

62

COME HOLY HARLEQUIN

Sydney Carter (1915–)   *Sydney Carter (1915–)*

Come ho - ly har - le - quin! Shake the world and shock that hy - po - crite. Rock, love, car - ry it a - way, Turn it up - side down. Let the peo - ple laugh and shout,— Let them in and let them out.— Rock, love, car - ry it a - way,— Turn it up - side down.

1 Come holy harlequin!
  Shake the world and shock that hypocrite.
  Rock, love, carry it away,
  Turn it upside down.
  Let the people laugh and shout,
  Let them in and let them out.
  Rock, love, carry it away,
  Turn it upside down.

2 Come holy harlequin!
  Shake that steeple, rock that synagogue.
  CHORUS
  Shock the scribe and pharisee,
  Shatter their monopoly.
  CHORUS

3 Come holy harlequin!
  Shake that graveyard, split that sepulchre.
  CHORUS
  Crack that clock that's killing me,
  Knock it to eternity.
  CHORUS

4 Leap, holy harlequin!
  Slap that stick and show your liberty.
  CHORUS
  Caper with your Columbine,
  Turn the water into wine.
  CHORUS

5 Rock, love, carry it away!
  Lift the world up by your levity.
  CHORUS
  Let the carnival begin,
  Let me out and let me in.
  CHORUS

63

COME ALL YOU MAKERS

Sydney Carter (1915—)   *Sydney Carter (1915—)*

1 Come all you makers of the world
And show me what you do.
I'll give to you the liberty
To be a maker too.
Oh! Come you makers of the world,
Sing with me today!
Oh! Share with me the liberty
To labour and to play.

2 I'll travel by your body
And I'll travel by your will,
I'll travel by your liberty,
I'll be a maker still.
CHORUS

3 I'll travel by the river
And I'll travel by the road,
The driving of a diesel
Or the lifting of a load.
CHORUS

4 I'll travel by the timber
And I'll travel by the steel,
The lifting of a hammer
And the turning of a wheel.
CHORUS

5 I'll travel by the teaching
And the learning of a trade,
The houses you are building
And the music you have made.
CHORUS

6 Come all you makers of the world,
I share the work with you,
I give to you the liberty
To be a maker too.
CHORUS

64

THERE COMES A GALLEY

Johann Tauler (1290–1361)
versified by G R Woodward (1848–1934)

from the Catholic Gesangbuch, Köln (1608)
as given by Frederick Layriz (1808–59)

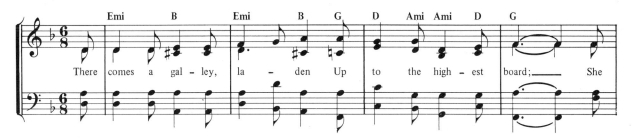

This carol may be sung in unison with keyboard or with guitar (in E minor). Two-part choirs may sing the top two parts unaccompanied or with piano; SAB sing parts as shown; SSA altos sing bass part an octave higher.

1 There comes a galley, laden
  Up to the highest board;
  She bears a heav'nly burthen,
  The Father's eterne Word.

2 She saileth on in silence,
  Her freight of value vast:
  With Charity for mainsail,
  And Holy Ghost for mast.

3 The ship hath dropt her anchor,
  Is safely come to land;
  The Word eterne, in likeness
  Of man, on earth doth stand.

4 At Beth'lem in a stable
  To save the world forlorn,
  (O bless Him for his mercy),
  Our Saviour Christ is born.

5 And whosoe'er with gladness
  Would kiss Him and adore
  Must first endure with Jesus
  Great pain and anguish sore,

6 Must die with Him moreover
  And rise in flesh again
  To win that life eternal
  Which doth to Christ pertain.

Reprinted by permission of A R Mowbray & Co. Ltd.

65

I WONDER AS I WANDER

Traditional American   *Traditional American*

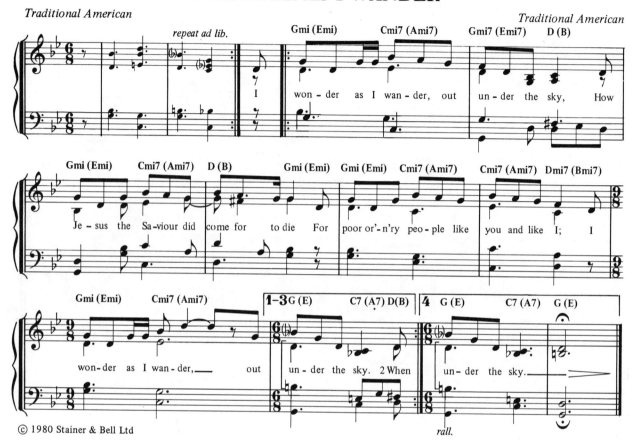

1 I wonder as I wander, out under the sky,
How Jesus the Saviour did come for to die
For poor or'n'ry people like you and like I;
I wonder as I wander, out under the sky.

2 When Mary birthed Jesus, 'twas in a cow's stall
With wise men and farmers and shepherds and all.
But high from God's heaven a star's light did fall,
And the promise of ages it did then recall.

3 If Jesus had wanted for any wee thing,
A star in the sky, or a bird on the wing,
Or all of God's angels in heaven for to sing,
He surely could have it, 'cause He was the King.

4 I wonder as I wander, out under the sky,
How Jesus the Saviour did come for to die
For poor or'n'ry people like you and like I;
I wonder as I wander, out under the sky.

Optional voices (humming) or instruments vv. 1 and 4

Apart from the optional lines in verses 1 and 4, verses may be sung by a soloist with ATB humming the three lower parts. Guitar chords are for use with soloist only; if the key is too difficult, play the chords in brackets with a capo on the third fret. SSA choirs may sing the tune with humming optional part.

66

JESUS BORN IN BETHLEHEM

Collected in North Carolina, USA
by Frank C Brown (1870–1943)

Traditional Kentucky

Reprinted with permission from the Frank C Brown Collection of North Carolina Folklore III.
© 1952 Duke University Press.
The words of this folk carol vary in metre in almost every verse. This is the basic tune and the singer(s) should choose the most natural way to fit the words of the story to it.

1 Jesus born in Bethlehem, *(three times)*
And in a manger lay. *(three times)*
Jesus born in Bethlehem
And in a manger lay.

2 His people crucified him
And nailed him on the cross.

3 Joseph begged his body
And laid it in the tomb.

4 The tomb would not hold it;
He burst the bars of death.

5 Mary came weeping
About her lovely Lord.

6 'What's the matter, Mary?'
'They've stole my Lord away.'

7 They found Jesus living,
Alive for evermore.

8 He ascended to his father
To reign with him on high.

Instrumental ostinato, repeated ad lib.

67

THE TWELVE JOYS OF MARY

Traditional Hampshire

Traditional English

v. 12

The first good joy that Ma — ry had, it was the joy____ of one;____ When
It was to see her own dear Son when He was born____ a man;____ When

He was born a man, good Lord,____ and bless — ings may it bring,____ Praise

Fa — ther, Son, and Ho — ly Ghost, to Christ's__ e — ter — ni — ty. O, the

CHORUS

ris — ing of the sun!____ The lift — ing of the day!____ While listen-ing to the

mer — its of gold And sing-ing in heaven al — way! Sing Al — le — lu — i — ah!____ Sing

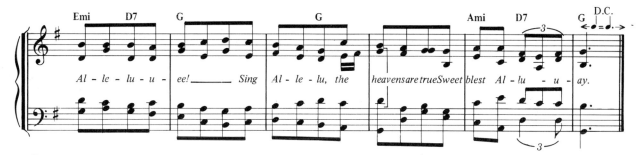

This carol may be sung in unison or solo with keyboard or with guitar. Verses and Chorus may be sung by SAB unaccompanied; tenors may sing Chorus to words 'O, the rising sun, lifting day, listening and singing in heaven alway!' and then as written.

1 The first good joy that Mary had, it was the joy of one;
It was to see her own dear Son when He was born a man;
When He was born a man, good Lord, and blessings may it bring,
Praise Father, Son, and Holy Ghost, to Christ's eternity.
O, the rising of the sun!
The lifting of the day!
While listening to the merits of gold
And singing in heaven alway!
Sing Allelu-i-ah!
Sing Allelu-u-ee!
Sing Allelu, the heavens are true,
Sweet blest Allu-u-ay.

2 The next good joy that Mary had, it was the joy of two;
It was the joy of her dear Son when He went on to school;
When He went on to school, good man, and blessings may it bring,
Praise Father, Son, and Holy Ghost, to Christ's eternity.
CHORUS

3 The next good joy that Mary had, it was the joy of three;
It was the joy of her dear Son when He began to read;
When He began to read, good man, and blessings may it bring,
Praise Father, Son, and Holy Ghost, to Christ's eternity.
CHORUS

4 The next good joy that Mary had, it was the joy of four,
It was to see her own dear Son to read the Bible o'er;
To read the Bible o'er, good man, and blessings may it bring,
Praise Father, Son, and Holy Ghost, to Christ's eternity.
CHORUS

5 The next good joy that Mary had, it was the joy of five;
It was to see her own dear Son turn water into wine;
Turn water into wine, good man, and blessings may it bring,
Praise Father, Son, and Holy Ghost, to Christ's eternity.
CHORUS

6 The next good joy that Mary had, it was the joy of six;
It was to see her own dear Son to cure the leprosy;
To cure the leprosy, good man, and blessings may it bring,
Praise Father, Son, and Holy Ghost, to Christ's eternity.
CHORUS

7 The next good joy that Mary had, it was the joy of seven;
It was the joy of her dear Son making the blind to see;
Making the blind to see, good man, and blessings may it bring,
Praise Father, Son, and Holy Ghost, to Christ's eternity.
CHORUS

8 The next good joy that Mary had, it was the joy of eight;
To see her own Son, Jesus, when He carried the crucifix;
When He carried the crucifix, and blessings may it bring,
Praise Father, Son, and Holy Ghost, to Christ's eternity.
CHORUS

9 The next good joy that Mary had, it was the joy of nine;
To see her own Son, Jesus, to from the dead arise;
To from the dead arise, good man, and blessings may it bring,
Praise Father, Son, and Holy Ghost, to Christ's eternity.
CHORUS

10 The next good joy that Mary had, it was the joy of ten;
To see her own Son, Jesus, to open the gates of hell;
To open the gates of hell, good man, and blessings may it bring,
Praise Father, Son, and Holy Ghost, to Christ's eternity.
CHORUS

11 The next good joy that Mary had, it was the joy of eleven;
It was the joy of her dear Son ascended into heaven;
Ascended into heaven, good man, and blessings may it bring,
Praise Father, Son, and Holy Ghost, to Christ's eternity.
CHORUS

12 The next good joy that Mary had, it was the joy of twelve;
It was the joy of her dear Son when the Holy Ghost was sent;
When the Holy Ghost was sent, good man, and blessings may it bring,
Praise Father, Son, and Holy Ghost, to Christ's eternity.
CHORUS

68

SAINTS DAY CAROL

Anonymous   *Traditional Cornish*

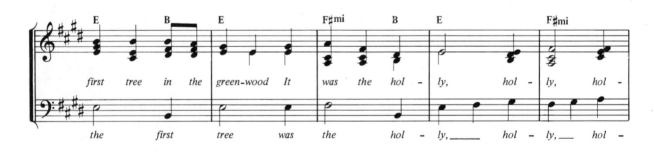

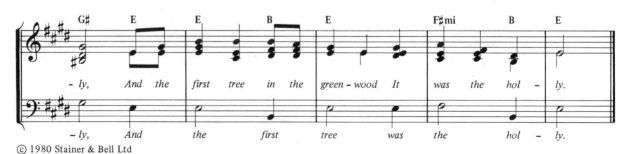

1 Now the holly bears a berry
   As white as the milk,
   And Mary bore Jesus
   Who was wrapped up in silk.
   And Mary bore Jesus Christ,
   Our Saviour to be,
   And the first tree in the greenwood
   It was the holly, holly, holly,
   And the first tree in the greenwood
   It was the holly.

2 Now the holly bears a berry
   As green as the grass,
   And Mary bore Jesus
   Who died on the Cross.
   CHORUS

3 Now the holly bears a berry
   As black as the coal,
   And Mary bore Jesus
   Who died for us all.
   CHORUS

4 Now the holly bears a berry
   As blood it is red,
   Then trust we our Saviour
   Who rose from the dead.
   CHORUS

69

SING LULLABY

S Baring-Gould (1834–1924)

Traditional Basque

1 Sing lullaby!
  Lullaby baby, now reclining,
  Sing lullaby!
  Hush, do not wake the Infant King.
  Angels are watching, stars are shining
  Over the place where he is lying:
  Sing lullaby!

2 Sing lullaby!
  Lullaby baby, now asleeping,
  Sing lullaby!
  Hush, do not wake the Infant King.
  Soon will come sorrow with the morning,
  Soon will come bitter grief and weeping:
  Sing lullaby!

3 Sing lullaby!
  Lullaby baby, now a-dozing,
  Sing lullaby!
  Hush, do not wake the Infant King.
  Soon comes the cross, the nails, the piercing,
  Then in the grave at last reposing:
  Sing lullaby!

4 Sing lullaby!
  Lullaby! Is the babe awaking?
  Sing lullaby!
  Hush, do not wake the Infant King.
  Dreaming of Easter, gladsome morning,
  Conquering death, its bondage breaking:
  Sing lullaby!

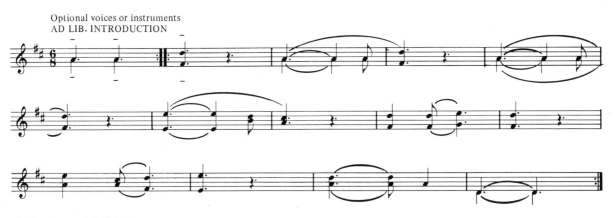

Optional voices or instruments
AD LIB. INTRODUCTION

This carol may be sung in unison or in two parts with keyboard or with guitar, or by SA and SAB groups with or without accompaniment and optional instruments; the vocalise may be used with unaccompanied singing or with accompaniment.

70

A CAROL FOR THE SUNDAY AFTER CHRISTMAS

Fred Pratt Green (1903–)   *Allen Percival (1925–)*

© 1980 Stainer & Bell Ltd

1 There's snow on the mountain and ice on the pond;
The Wise Men are home now in the back of beyond;
The Shepherds have left us; the heavens are dumb:
There's no one to tell us why Jesus has come.

2 The tree drops its needles, as sign we must go;
But the long road to Egypt lies covered in snow;
And wherever we travel the food will be dear:
Who knows what's before us this coming New Year?

3 But God's in his heaven, and Jesus has come
To show every sinner he is welcome back home,
To be this world's Saviour from hunger and fear,
And give us new courage to face the New Year.

71

MARY'S CHILD

Geoffrey Ainger (1925–)   *Geoffrey Ainger (1925–)*

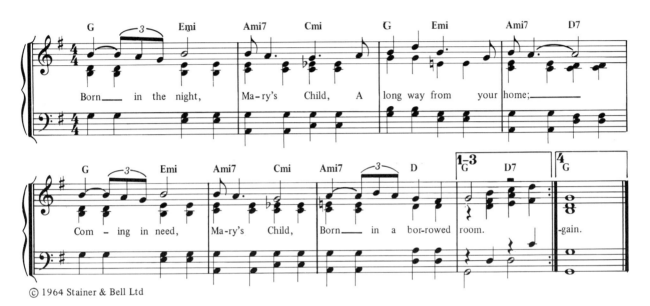

1 Born in the night,
Mary's Child,
A long way from your home;
Coming in need,
Mary's Child,
Born in a borrowed room.

2 Clear shining light,
Mary's Child,
Your face lights up our way;
Light of the world,
Mary's Child,
Dawn on our darkened day.

3 Truth of our life,
Mary's Child,
You tell us God is good;
Prove it is true,
Mary's Child,
Go to your cross of wood.

4 Hope of the world,
Mary's Child,
You're coming soon to reign;
King of the earth,
Mary's Child,
Walk in our streets again.

Optional instruments

72
RING THE BELLS

Fred Pratt Green (1903–)   *Traditional, eighteenth-century French*

Ring the bells of__ Beth-le - hem!
Je-sus is born to__ save us all:__
Comes to re-deem us__
from the Fall:__

Ring the bells in__ ev-ery town,
There is joy when the lost are found.__
Let the whole world__
hear the sound!__

Optional 'bell' instruments:

144

1 Ring the bells of Bethlehem!
  Jesus is born to save us all:
  Ring the bells of Bethlehem!
  Comes to redeem us from the Fall.
  Ring the bells of every town,
  There is joy when the lost are found.
  Ring the bells in every town,
  Let the whole world hear the sound!

2 Toll a bell in Jerusalem!
  Jesus dies to save us all,
  Toll a bell in Jerusalem!
  Dies to redeem us from the Fall.
  CHORUS

3 Ring the bells of Jerusalem!
  Jesus lives to save us all:
  Ring the bells of Jerusalem!
  Lives to redeem us from the Fall.
  CHORUS

4 Ring the bells of every town!
  Let the whole world hear the sound!
  Ring the bells of every town!
  There is joy that the lost are found!

NOTE: In verse 4, the name of your town may be used, if it fits.

73

COVENTRY CAROL

In the Pageant of the Shearman and Tailors,
fifteenth century

Anonymous 1591

Lul - ly, lul - la, thou lit - tle ti - ny child, By by, lul -

- ly, lul - lay, thou lit - tle ti - ny child, By by, lul -

- ly lul - lay. O sis - ters too, how may we do

For to pre - serve this day This poor young - ling for

whom we do sing, By by, lul — ly lul — lay?

Large notes show the original manuscript version, meant for Alto Tenor and Bass but here given for SAB. The small notes in the right hand near the end are probably what the scribe intended; the clash between F♮ and F♯ was not impossible at the time, however. Small notes in the left hand are added to make an unaccompanied SATB verse and/or chorus possible.

Lully, lulla, thou little tiny child,
By by, lully, lullay, thou little tiny child,
By by, lully lullay.

1 O sisters too, how may we do
  For to preserve this day
  This poor youngling for whom we do sing,
  By by, lully lullay?
  CHORUS

2 Herod the king, in his raging,
  Chargèd he hath this day
  His men of might, in his own sight,
  All young children to slay.
  CHORUS

3 That woe is me, poor child for thee!
  And ever mourn and say,
  For thy parting neither say nor sing
  By by, lully lullay.
  CHORUS

NOTE: The words are called 'The Lullaby by the mothers of the Innocents' in the Coventry play.

147

74

ORIENTIS PARTIBUS (THE DONKEY'S CAROL)

Fred Pratt Green (1903–)

Twelfth-century French

Here's a don-key you may trust; While you can, es-

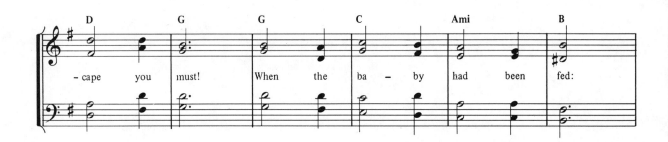

-cape you must! When the ba — by had been fed:

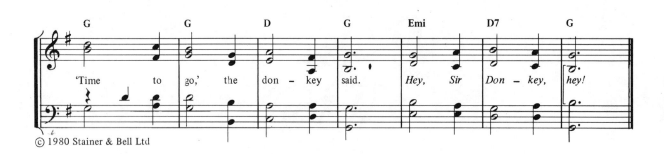

'Time to go,' the don-key said. Hey, Sir Don-key, hey!

This carol may be sung in unison with keyboard or with guitar. SAB choirs may sing the parts as written: SS or SA sing top two parts with or without accompaniment or to a drum rhythm of ♩ ♩ throughout; SSA altos sing bass part an octave higher.

1 Here's a donkey you may trust;
  While you can, escape you must!
  When the baby had been fed:
  'Time to go,' the donkey said.
  Hey, Sir Donkey, hey!

2 Every day they lived in dread.
  Little Saviour, make no sound;
  Wicked men are prowling round!
  'Watch your step,' the donkey said.
  Hey, Sir Donkey, hey!

3 Out of Egypt, Israel fled;
  Back to Egypt, they must go.
  Soft the sand, the going slow:
  'Take your time,' the donkey said.
  Hey, Sir Donkey, hey!

4 When the donkey disobeyed,
  Joseph raised his stick in wrath.
  There is danger in our path—
  'Think of Balaam,' Mary said,
  Hey, Sir Donkey, hey!

5 Where's the manna, magic bread?
  Where's the water Moses struck
  For the thirsty, out of rock?
  'Trust in God,' the donkey said.
  Hey, Sir Donkey, hey!

6 Look, a city shines ahead!
  Look at all the houses there!
  Will they vanish into air?
  'Time will show,' the donkey said.
  Hey, Sir Donkey, hey!

7 Safe they are, with bed and board;
  Safe and sound, our little Lord.
  Till, at last, King Herod dead,
  'Home we go,' the donkey said.
  Hey, Sir Donkey, hey!

NOTE: The Latin Carol was originally a Pilgrims' Song used on the route to Compostela and later was sung in France on 14 January each year at the Festival of the Donkey which commemorated the flight of the Holy Family into Egypt. This use has prompted the modern version printed here.

1 Orientis partibus
  Adventavit asinus,
  Pulcher et fortissimus,
  Sarcinis aptissimus.
  Hez, sire Ane, hez.

2 Aurum de Arabia
  Thus et myrrham de Saba,
  Tulit in ecclesia
  Virtus asinaria.
  Hez, sire Ane, hez.

3 Amen, dicas, asine;
  Iam satur de gramine;
  Amen, amen itera,
  Aspernare vetera.
  Hez, sire Ane, hez.

Optional instrument(s) or voices

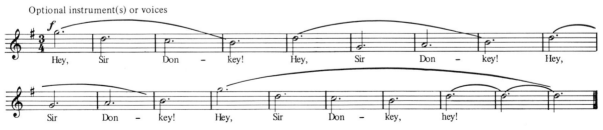

Hey, Sir Don - key! Hey, Sir Don - key! Hey,
Sir Don - key! Hey, Sir Don - key, hey!

149

75

THE PRODIGAL COMES HOME

Chris Rogers (1922–)
from the Swedish by Anders Frostenson (1906–)

Peter D. Smith (1938–)

He came from a far-a-way land And he knew not that love was at hand. He looked none in the face,___ He felt on-ly dis-grace,___ For he saw not for--give-ness, but shame.___ Put a ring on his hand and Shoes on his feet, Put a ring on his hand and Shoes on his feet, Let's be mer-ry and dance and Make him a feast, Let's be merry and make him a feast.___

1 He came from a far-away land
  And he knew not that love was at hand.
  He looked none in the face,
  He felt only disgrace,
  For he saw not forgiveness, but shame.
  Put a ring on his hand and
  Shoes on his feet,
  Put a ring on his hand and
  Shoes on his feet,
  Let's be merry and dance and
  Make him a feast,
  Let's be merry and make him a feast.

2 He arrives within sight of his home,
  There's rapturous welcome to come,
  Someone's meeting him now,
  Someone's greeting him now,
  And he knows he's no longer alone.
  CHORUS

3 The agonised days are all gone,
  Life returns to the prodigal son.
  Taken back to the fold,
  He finds blessings untold
  Where creation is gathered in one.
  CHORUS

76

DIVES AND LAZARUS

Traditional Herefordshire

Traditional Herefordshire
Arranged by R Vaughan Williams (1872—1958)

1 As it fell out up – on one day, Rich Di – vus made a feast, And he in – vit – ed all his friends And gen-try of the best. 2 Then Laz – 'rus laid him down and down, And down at Di – vus' door, 'Some

meat and drink, bro-ther Di — ver-us, Be - stow up - on the poor.' 3 'Thou'rt year.

Guitar chords are for use with melody only in the key of G.

1 As it fell out upon one day,
   Rich Divus made a feast,
   And he invited all his friends
   And gentry of the best.

2 Then Laz'rus laid him down and down,
   And down at Divus' door,
   'Some meat and drink, brother Diverus,
   Bestow upon the poor.'

3 'Thou'rt none of mine, brother Lazarus
   That liest begging at my door,
   No meat, nor drink will I give thee,
   Nor bestow upon the poor.'

(Continued overleaf)
153

4 Then Laz'rus laid him down and down,
   All under Divus' wall,
   'Some meat, some drink, brother Diverus,
   For hunger starve I shall.'

5 'Thou'rt none of mine, brother Lazarus,
   That liest begging at my wall,
   No meat, nor drink will I give thee,
   For hunger starve you shall.'

6 Then Laz'rus laid him down and down,
   And down at Divus' gate,
   'Some meat! some drink! brother Diverus,
   For Jesus Christ His sake.'

7 'Thou'rt none of mine, brother Lazarus,
   That liest begging at my gate,
   No meat, no drink will I give thee,
   For Jesus Christ His sake.'

8 Then Divus sent out his hungry dogs
   To worry poor Laz'rus away;
   They hadn't the power to bite one bite
   But licked his sores away.

9 Then Divus sent to his merry men
   To worry poor Laz'rus away;
   They'd not the power to strike one stroke
   But flung their whips away.

10 As it fell out upon one day,
   Poor Laz'rus sickened and died,
   There came two angels out of Heaven,
   His soul therein to guide.

11 'Rise up! rise up! brother Lazarus,
   And go along with me,
   For you've a place prepared in Heaven
   To sit on an angel's knee.'

12 As it fell out upon one day,
   Rich Divus sickened and died,
   There came two serpents out of Hell,
   His soul therein to guide.

13 'Rise up! rise up! brother Diverus
   And come along with me,
   There is a place provided in Hell
   For wicked men like thee.'

14 And now my carol's ended,
   No longer can I stay here;
   God bless you all, both great and small,
   And God send you a happy new year.

77

TIME IS FULL TO OVERFLOWING

Fred Kaan (1929–) from the Swedish of
Lars Thunberg (1928–)

Ingmar Milveden (1920–)

Time is full to o-ver-flow-ing,___ Trees are new-ly dressed in green.

Through the land the news is spread-ing:___ God___ will come to reign.___

Printed by permission of the composer and Ab verbum, Stockholm.

1 Time is full to overflowing,
   Trees are newly dressed in green.
   Through the land the news is spreading:
   God will come to reign.

2 In the hope to know tomorrow,
   Eyes are turned to scan the sky,
   Terrified by night and lightning,
   Storm and raging tide.

3 Day is nearing when the nations
   Will be tested for their worth.
   Watch and pray against temptation;
   All will be unearthed.

4 He, the Judge, who is our gladness,
   Now is standing at the door:
   Jesus will be born of woman,
   Jesus will be Lord.

5 See him hour by hour advancing,
   Marching through the Christian year;
   He whom clouds will bear to heaven,
   Christ, the man, is here.

6 In our hands he lays the tokens,
   Kingly gifts of bread and wine,
   Raising us to life eternal
   Out of death's domain.

7 No-one knows the days and seasons
   When the kingdom is to come;
   Build as if it came tomorrow,
   Be awake, make room!

78

STANDING ON OUR THRESHOLD THREADBARE

Traditional French 'Jesus Christ s'habille en pauvre'
English Version by Bernard A Braley (1924—)

Traditional French,
known as 'Picardy'

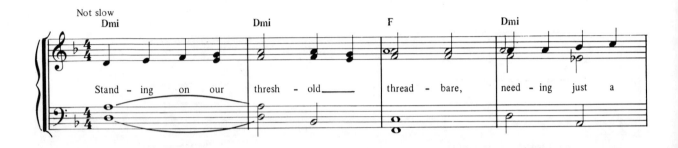

Stand - ing on our thresh - old_____ thread - bare, need - ing just a

sim - ple_____ meal, Je - sus Christ him - self is_____ wait - ing,

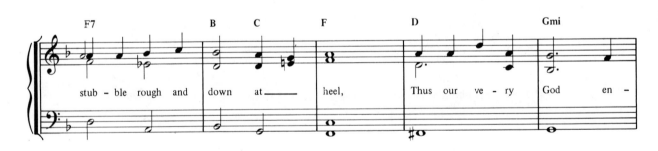

stub - ble rough and down at_____ heel, Thus our ve - ry God en -

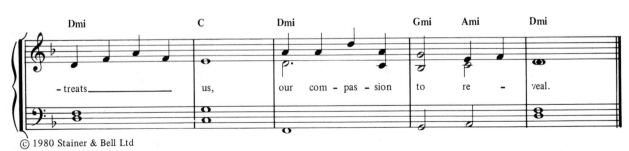

- treats_____ us, our com - pas - sion to re - veal.

1 Standing on our threshold threadbare, needing just a simple meal,
Jesus Christ himself is waiting, stubble rough and down at heel,
Thus our very God entreats us, our compassion to reveal.

2 Eyeing up and down this vagrant, 'Worthless man of that I'm sure,
Poor investment for the future', notes the husband at the door.
'I will give the dogs our leavings: they will hunt and bring us more.'

3 Turned away by callous husband, needing still a simple meal,
Jesus turns toward the window, stubble rough and down at heel,
Hears kind words of cheerful greeting, wife's compassion to reveal.

4 Soon he's settled in the guest-room, with a pillow for his head,
Vagrant Christ himself is sleeping, resting in a well-aired bed,
Dreaming of her homely comforts, gracious thoughts and fresh-baked bread.

5 Angels on the moonlit staircase tell the woman she'll soon die,
But with Jesus Christ the Saviour live in Paradise on high,
While her grasping, selfish husband trapped in fires of Hell shall fry!

NOTE: In the following French original, follow the poetic syllables, giving full value to words ending in pronouncing vowels, such as 'pau-vre', 'ta-ble', 'rappor-tent', 'qu'et-tes', 'eu-rent' etc. Small notes in the music are for use with the French of verses 5 and 6.

1 Jésus Christ s'habille en pauvre. 'Faites moi la charité. (*twice*)
Des miettes de votre table, je ferais bien mon dîner.'

2 'Les miettes de notre table, nos chiens les mangeront bien. (*twice*)
Ils nous rapportent de lièvres. Toi, tu ne rapportes rien.'

3 'Madame, qu'ettes en fenêtre, faites-moi la charité,' (*twice*)
'Ah, montez, montez, bon pauvre. Avec moi vous souperez.'

4 Après qu'ils eurent tous soupés, il demande à se coucher. (*twice*)
'Ah, montez, montez, bon pauvre. Un lit frais vous trouverez.'

5 Comme ils montaient les degrés, trois beaux anges les éclairaient. (*twice*)
'Ah, ne craignez rien, Madame, c'est la lune qui parait.'

6 'Dans trois jours vous mourerez. En Paradis vous irez. (*twice*)
Et votre mari, Madame, en enfer ira brûler.'

Optional instruments or vocalise

79

THE HOLY WELL

Traditional Herefordshire

Traditional Herefordshire
Arranged by R Vaughan Williams (1872–1958)

Guitar chords are for use with melody only in the key of G.

1 As it fell out upon a day,
　On a high and a holy day,
　Sweet Jesus asked of His mother dear
　If he might go and play.

2 'To play, to play, sweet Jesus shall go,
　To play now get You gone,
　And let me hear of no complaints
　Tonight when You come home.'

3 Sweet Jesus went down to yonder town,
　As far as the Holy Well,
　And there did He see as fine children
　As any tongue can tell.

4 He bade God bless them, every one,
　And Christ their portion be.
　'Little children, shall I play with you?
　And you shall play with Me.'

5 'O nay we are lords' and ladies' sons,
　Born in bower and hall,
　And You the meanest of us all
　Born in an ox's stall.'

6 Sweet Jesus turned Himself around,
　And neither did laugh nor smile,
　But the tears did fall from sweet Jesus' eyes,
　Like water from the sky.

7 Sweet Jesus turned himself around,
　To His mother home went He,
　He said, 'I have been to yonder town
　As far as you can see.'

8 'I have been down to yonder town,
　As far as the Holy Well,
　And there did see as fine children
　As any tongue can tell.'

9 'I bid God bless them every one
　And their bodies Christ save and see,
　Little children, shall I play with you,
　And you shall play with Me.'

10 'O nay we are lords' and ladies' sons
　Born in bower and hall,
　And You, the meanest of us all,
　Were born in ox's stall.'

11 'Sweet Jesus, go down yonder town
　As far as the Holy Well,
　And take away those sinful souls,
　And dip them deep in Hell.'

12 'Nay, nay,' sweet Jesus smiled and said,
　'Nay, nay, that must not be,
　For there are too many sinful souls
　Crying out for the help of Me.'

13 Then up spoke the Angel Gabriel,
　'Now by our good Saint Stephen,
　Although Thou art but a maiden's child,
　Thou art the King of Heaven.'

159

80

LORD JESUS PLANTS HIS GARDEN

Jesus' Bloemhof, 1633 Dutch
English version by Bernard A Braley (1924–)

Traditional Dutch,
probably seventeenth century

© 1980 Stainer & Bell Ltd

This carol may be sung solo or in unison with keyboard or with guitar. Verses and chorus may be sung unaccompanied by SA or SAB groups, with or without the instrumental line.

1 Lord Jesus plants his garden,
  Rich with fertile seed
  For perfumed rainbow harvest,
  Flower for every need.
On hallowed ground let's merrily sound with resonant flute,
With joy, pipe on a ring-dance song with cymbal, lyre and lute,
With joy, pipe on a ring-dance song with cymbal, lyre and lute.

2 Lord Jesus plants a Lily,
  Pure as morning dew,
  And sweetly scented Violet,
  Humbly hid from view.
  CHORUS

3 Lord Jesus prunes his Roses,
  Signs of self control
  While ordered rows of Marigold
  Highlight reason's role.
  CHORUS

4 Lord Jesus tends three bushes,
  Prized above the rest,
  He names them Faith and Hopeful;
  Love he names the best.
  CHORUS

5 The Lord plants in his garden
  Lives of human kind,
  He plants his seed within us,
  Claims each heart and mind.
  CHORUS

© 1980 Stainer & Bell Ltd

81

THE CLOCK CAROL

Paul Townsend (1923–)   *Donald Swann (1923–)*

When the bells chime noon in Lon - don New York be - gins its day, Good morn - ing in Tor - on - to spells Good - night for Man - da - lay. When the

sun shines on the py – ram – ids Al – as – ka's in the dark: At

one tick of the clock God hears Both night – in – gale and lark. For

He is there through nights and days, Through rain and cold and heat; Be –

–hind the chat – ter of the clocks We sense His time – less beat.

Mid - day mid - night, the bells are al - ways ring - ing,

legato

The world keeps turn - ing in - to day and night;

Sun - shine, moon - shine, the light and sha - dow bring - ing,

Pat - terns they make from God's one light. While some

poco rit.

poco rit.

Ped. Ped.

Ped.

163

men work at their bench-es Their bro-thers work in fields, Yet

one Cre-a-tor is the source Of what their la-bour yields. Men

of all kinds and co-lours, In fac-to-ry or field, Have

on their fa-ces black or white, God's i-mage there re-vealed. For

164

East and West in Him are one, And col - our, race and clime;

His love will reach be - yond the bounds Of night and day and time.

82

A TROUBADOUR'S CAROL

Fred Pratt Green (1903–)

Allen Percival (1925–)

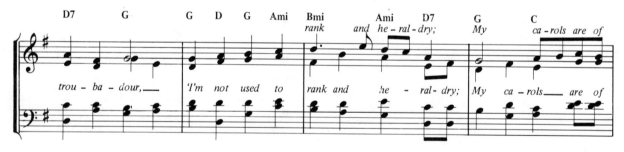

It is suggested that the introduction is sung to the tune of the verse in unison by the whole choir or by a soloist, perhaps unaccompanied. Verses and Chorus may then be sung by alternate groups from the choir (in unison or in parts) or by two alternating soloists.

Introduction
Hear how one Christian troubadour
So pleased his liege Lord,
He told his heralds to prepare
Knight's arms as his reward.

1 'Let them decide what shape his shield,
What colour it should be:
Gules, azure, sable, vert, the field—
It matters not,' he said, 'to me.'
'Sire,' cried the troubadour,
'I'm not used to rank and heraldry;
My carols are of Jesus Christ:
No coat of arms had he.'

2 'As for device, we do direct
A lion shall he display:
But rampant, couchant, or erect—
It is for him alone to say.'
CHORUS

3 'Above his helm, mantling and torse
Shall show; but as for crest:
A stag or swan or hare or horse—
Or anything that suits him best.'
CHORUS

4 'His two supporters, men or beasts,
With or without a soul,
If panthers, pelicans or priests,
Must be well-balanced on a scroll.'
CHORUS

5 'Unwed, impalement would be wrong;
No quarterings apply:
A motto in the Latin tongue
My learned heralds shall supply.'
'Sire,' cried the troubadour,
'I'm not used to rank and heraldry;
Humblest of Lords was Jesus Christ:
What he was, I must be!'

83

THE CARNAL AND THE CRANE

Words as collected by Francis J Child (1825–1896)

Traditional Herefordshire
Arranged by R Vaughan Williams (1872–1958)

1 As I passed by a riverside, And there as I did reign In argument I chanced to hear A Carnal and a Crane.

2 The Carnal said unto the Crane, 'If all the world should turn, Be-

Guitar chords are for use without piano only.
This carol may be sung in four episodes by singing these additional verses to parts A B *or* C *of the musical arrangement as shown, fitting the syllables as easily as pronunciation:*

Episode 1

THE CARNAL AND THE CRANE
(Continued)

A 4 'I pray thee,' said the Carnal,
'Tell me before thou go,
Was not the mother of Jesus
Conceived by the Holy Ghost?'

B 5 'She was the purest virgin,
And the cleanest from sin;
She was the handmaid of our Lord
And mother of our king.'

C 6 'Where is the golden cradle
That Christ was rocked in?
Where are the silken sheets
That Jesus was wrapt in?'

C 7 'A manger was the cradle
That Christ was rocked in:
The provender the asses left
So sweetly he slept on.'

169

Episode 2

THE WISE MEN AND HEROD

[A] 8 There was a star in the east land,
So bright it did appear,
Into King Herod's chamber,
And where King Herod were.

[B] 9 The Wise Men soon espied it,
And told the king on high
A princely babe was born that night
No king could e'er destroy.

[C] 10 'If this be true,' King Herod said,
'As thou tellest unto me,
This roasted cock that lies in the dish
Shall crow full fences three.'

[A] 11 The cock soon freshly feathered was,
By the work of God's own hand,
And then three fences crowed he,
In the dish where he did stand.

[B] 12 'Rise up, rise up, you merry men all,
See that you ready be;
All children under two years old
Now slain they all shall be.'

Episode 3

JESUS AND THE BEASTS

[A] 13 Then Jesus, ah, and Joseph,
And Mary, that was so pure,
They travelled into Egypt,
And you shall find it sure.

[B] 14 And when they came to Egypt's land,
Amongst those fierce wild beasts,
Mary, she being weary,
Must needs sit down to rest.

[C] 15 'Come sit thee down,' says Jesus,
'Come sit thee down by me,
And thou shalt see how these wild beasts
Do come and worship me.'

[A] 16 First came the lovely lion,
Which Jesus's grace did bring,
And of the wild beasts in the field
The lion shall be king.

[B] 17 We'll choose our virtuous princes
Of birth and high degree,
In every sundry nation,
Where'er we come and see.

Episode 4

JESUS AND THE HUSBANDMAN

[A] 18 Then Jesus, ah, and Joseph,
And Mary, that was unknown,
They travelled by a husbandman,
Just while his seed was sown.

[B] 19 'God speed thee, man,' said Jesus,
'Go fetch thy ox and wain,
And carry home thy corn again
Which thou this day hast sown.'

[C] 20 The husbandman fell on his knees,
Even upon his face:
'Long time hast thou been lookèd for,
But now thou art come at last.

[A] 21 And I myself do now believe
Thy name is Jesus called;
Redeemer of mankind thou art,
Though undeserving all.'

[B] 22 'The truth, man, thou hast spoken,
Of it thou mayst be sure,
For I must lose my precious blood
For thee and thousands more.

[C] 23 If anyone should come this way,
And enquire for me alone,
Tell them that Jesus passed by
As thou thy seed did sow.'

[A] 24 After that there came King Herod,
With his train so furiously,
Enquiring of the husbandman
Whether Jesus passed by.

[B] 25 'Why, the truth it must be spoke,
And the truth it must be known;
For Jesus passed by this way
When my seed was sown.

[C] 26 But now I have it reapen,
And some laid on my wain,
Ready to fetch and carry
Into my barn again.'

[A] 27 'Turn back' says the captain,
'Your labour and mine's in vain;
It's full three quarters of a year
Since he his seed has sown.'

[B] 28 So Herod was deceived,
By the work of God's own hand,
And further he proceeded
Into the Holy Land.

[C] 29 There's thousands of children young
Which for his sake did die;
Do not forbid those little ones,
And do not them deny.

[C] 30 The truth now I have spoken,
And the truth now I have shown;
Even the Blessed Virgin
She's now brought forth a son.

84

CAROL OF SAINT STAFFAN

Translated by E Bliss Reed (1872–1940)

Traditional Swedish
Arranged by David Stanley Smith (1877–1940)

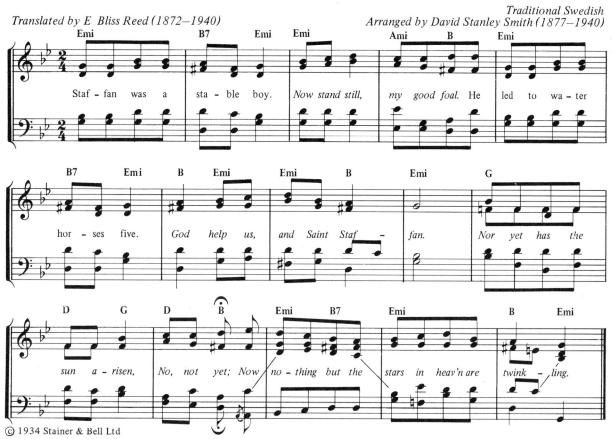

© 1934 Stainer & Bell Ltd

This carol may be sung in unison with keyboard or with guitar (in E minor).

1 Staffan was a stable boy
Now stand still, my good foal.
He led to water horses five.
God help us, and Saint Staffan.
Not yet has the sun arisen,
No, not yet;
Now nothing but the stars in heav'n are twinkling.

2 His fifth one was dapple gray....
That horse it is that Staffan rides....

3 Long before the cock has crowed....
Within the stable Staffan's gone....

4 Fast he saddles his good horse....
Before the sun is in the sky....

5 Hunting in the woods he's gone....
So early, no one was awake....

6 When the day of hunting ends....
The foal returns unto his home....

7 Now the fire is on the hearth....
There's Christmas porridge, Christmas pig....

8 Yeoman, satisfied and glad....
Are dancing polkas round and round....

9 Flushed and warm the mother stands....
Her child she's holding in her arms....

10 Julen ends, my brother Knut....
For now my song draws to its close....

85
TRAVELLING WITH GOD

Sydney Carter (1915–)   *Sydney Carter (1915–)*

One more step a-long the world I go,
One more step a-long the world I go.
From the old things to the new Keep me tra-vel-ling a-long with you. *And it's*
from the old I tra-vel to the new, Keep me tra-vel-ling a-long with you.

v.5 voices or instruments

1 One more step along the world I go,
   One more step along the world I go.
   From the old things to the new
   Keep me travelling along with you.
   And it's from the old I travel to the new,
   Keep me travelling along with you.

2 Round the corner of the world I turn,
   More and more about the world I learn.
   All the new things that I see
   You'll be looking at along with me.
   CHORUS

3 As I travel through the bad and good
   Keep me travelling the way I should.
   Where I see no way to go
   You'll be telling me the way, I know.
   CHORUS

4 Give me courage when the world is rough,
   Keep me loving though the world is tough.
   Leap and sing in all I do,
   Keep me travelling along with you.
   CHORUS

5 You are older than the world can be,
   You are younger than the life in me.
   Ever old and ever new,
   Keep me travelling along with you.
   CHORUS

173

86

IN THE LOOKING GLASS OF FRANCIS

Sydney Carter (1915—)   *Sydney Carter (1915—)*

Lilting, but not too fast

mf

In the look - ing glass of Fran - cis It's a young man that I see And he's pi - ping for the dan - cers In the fields of Ga-li-lee, In the fields of Ga-li-lee.

2 Did you

This carol may be sung with keyboard or with guitar. If voices do not need the melody played, the keyboard part sounds well throughout if the melody is omitted.

1 In the looking glass of Francis
  It's a young man that I see
  And he's piping for the dancers
  In the fields of Galilee,
  In the fields of Galilee.

2 Did you dance and did you revel
  Till the night became the day
  Like the young man of Assisi?
  Mark and Matthew never say,
  Mark and Matthew never say.

3 In the looking glass of Francis
  It's a young man that I see
  And the Romans go a-riding
  Through the fields of Galilee,
  Through the fields of Galilee.

4 Were you always meek and gentle?
  Francis longed to be a knight.
  Did you never wonder whether
  You should take the sword to fight,
  You should take the sword to fight?

5 In the looking glass of Francis
  It's a young man that I see
  And the lovers go a-laughing
  Through the fields of Galilee,
  Through the fields of Galilee.

6 Did you never love a woman
  Like the young men of today
  With your soul and with your body?
  Mark and Matthew never say,
  Mark and Matthew never say.

7 Mark and Matthew never tell me,
  Luke and John are silent too
  When I ask them for the story
  Of the young man that was you,
  Of the young man that was you.

8 In the looking glass of Francis
  It's a young man that I see
  And he's piping for the dancers
  In the fields of Galilee,
  In the fields of Galilee.

87

THE LOST IS FOUND

Cecily Taylor (1930–)

Traditional Austrian
adapted by John Maynard (1925–)

Where, oh where's my sil – ver piece? Where, oh where? Where, oh where? Where, oh where's my sil – ver piece?

Where, oh where's it gone? Search-ing high and search-ing low, Search-ing high, search-ing low;

Oh, what joy when it is found! Joy when it is found! Let's join hands and dance for joy,

Stamp for joy, clap for joy; Let's join hands and dance for joy, Stamp and clap for joy!

1 Where, oh where's my silver piece?
Where, oh where? Where, oh where?
Where, oh where's my silver piece?
Where, oh where's it gone?
Searching high and searching low,
Searching high, searching low;
Oh, what joy when it is found!
Joy when it is found!
Let's join hands and dance for joy,
Stamp for joy, clap for joy;
Let's join hands and dance for joy,
Stamp and clap for joy!

2 Where, oh where's my little lamb?
Where, oh where? Where, oh where?
Where, oh where's my little lamb?
Where, oh where's he gone?
Searching here and searching there,
Searching here, searching there;
Oh what joy when he is found,
Joy when he is found!
CHORUS

3 Where, oh where's my wand'ring son?
Where, oh where? Where, oh where?
Where, oh where's my wand'ring son?
Where, oh where's he gone?
Looking far and looking long,
Looking far, looking long,
Oh, what joy when he comes home,
Joy when he comes home?
CHORUS

88

LISTEN

Brian Frost (1935–)

Traditional Northumberland
adapted June Tillman (1943–)

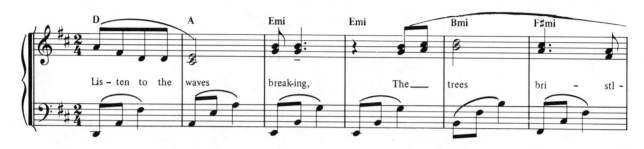

Lis – ten to the waves   break-ing,   The___ trees   bri – stl-

-ing;___   Lis – ten to the sea–gull's   din,   See the

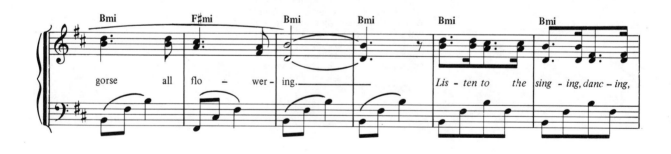

gorse   all flo – wer–ing.___   Lis – ten to the sing – ing, danc – ing,

Christ with – in,   *Lis – ten to the Christ   with – in.*___

1 Listen to the waves breaking,
  The trees bristling;
  Listen to the sea-gulls' din,
  See the gorse all flowering.
  Listen to the singing, dancing,
  Christ within,
  Listen to the Christ within.

2 Listen to the wind blowing,
  The woods glistering;
  Listen to the hooting owl,
  Hear the animals all growl.
  CHORUS

3 Listen to the city roaring,
  The paths whistling;
  Listen to the children call,
  Watch the melting snow-flake fall.
  CHORUS

Optional instruments

89

TEMPUS ADEST FLORIDUM

Anonymous. English version by Bernard A Braley (1924—)   *Melody in 'Piae Cantiones' (1582)*

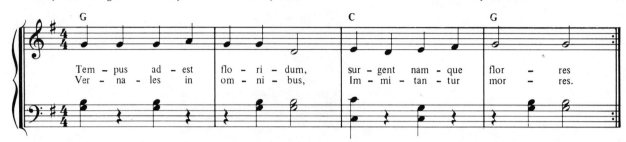

Tem - pus ad - est flo - ri - dum, sur - gent nam - que flor - res
Ver - na - les in om - ni - bus, Im - mi - tan - tur mor - res.

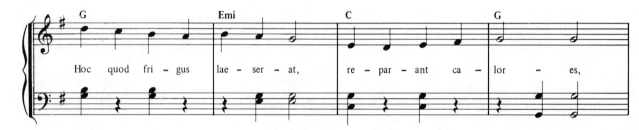

Hoc quod fri - gus lae - ser - at, re - par - ant ca - lor - es,

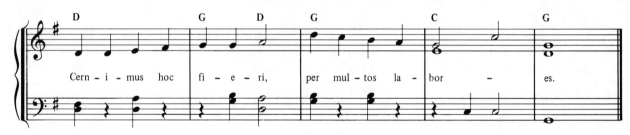

Cern - i - mus hoc fi - e - ri, per mul - tos la - bor - es.

By following the guitar chords a vocal backing can be provided as follows:

G   C   Emi   D

Optional voices or instruments. The lower part is for any plucked stringed instrument with open strings D, E, & G (at any pitch).

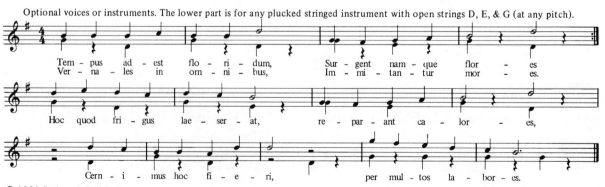

Tem - pus ad - est flo - ri - dum, Sur - gent nam - que flor - es
Ver - na - les in om - ni - bus, Im - mi - tan - tur mor - res

Hoc quod fri - gus lae - ser - at, re - par - ant ca - lor - es,

Cern - i - mus hoc fi - e - ri, per mul - tos la - bor - es.

1 Tempus adest floridum, surgent namque flores
  Vernales in omnibus, imitantur mores,
  Hoc quod frigus laeserat, reparant calores,
  Cernimus hoc fieri, per multos labores.

2 Prata plena floribus jucunda aspectu,
  Ubi juvat cernere herbas cum delectu
  Gramina et plantae quae hyeme quiescunt,
  Vernali in tempore vivunt et accrescunt.

3 Haec vobis pulcre monstrant Deum Creatorem,
  Quem quoque nos credimus omnium factorem:
  Tempus ergo hilare, quo laetari libet,
  Renovato nam mundo, nos novari decet.

4 Res ornatur floribus et multo decore,
  Nos honestis moribus et vero amore,
  Gaudeamus igitur tempore jucundo,
  Laudemusque Dominum pectoris ex fundo.

NOTES: cer = sher   accrescunt = accre-shunt   ae = ay   j = y   decet = de-shet

1 Snowdrop, crocus, daffodil,
  Freed from Winter's tether,
  Born again from bulbous womb,
  Coaxed by Spring-like weather.
  Call us from despair and doubt,
  With new growth restore us
  That we greet with fresh-born hope
  Life's that set before us.

2 Flow'ring shrub and orchard tree,
  Freed from Winter's tether,
  Dressed in varied finery
  Forming Spring together,
  Teach us, born of diverse seed,
  Teach us by your blending
  That we need each tribe and clan,
  Each on each depending.

3 Flora, fauna, cell on cell,
  Knit by God together,
  Death defied by constant birth
  In all seasons' weather—
  Chided we the barren earth
  Faithless with derision?
  Thanks be to the Lord of Life
  For Spring's lush provision.

4 Patience, Humour, Love and Joy,
  Freed from Evil's tether, ,
  Born again in mortals' souls
  In life's varied weather—
  Praise God when these choke the weeds
  Made by nightmare factions,
  When fine words of good intent
  Generate fine actions.

89a

CHRISTIAN AID

NOTE: This reflection on the familiar 'Good King Wenceslas' words is sung to the tune 'Tempus Adest Floridum'.

1 Once upon a time they went,
  King and page together,
  On a deed of kindness bent,
  In the winter weather.
  Every legend, has its truth,
  May this one remind us
  Where a neighbour is in need
  Christ expects to find us.

2 Victims of injustice cry:
  On your own confession
  Charity is not enough,
  We must end oppression.
  Yet, in such a world as this,
  Daily we are proving
  There are evils none can cure
  Without deeds of loving.

3 We must follow in his steps
  Who was found in fashion
  As a man, yet never lost
  His divine compassion.
  Lord, release such love in us,
  We shall be more ready
  To reach out with speedy aid
  To your poor and needy.

Fred Pratt Green (1903–   )

90

PRAISE GOD, TELL HIS GRACE

Bernard A Braley (1924–)

Traditional Sicilian

Praise God, tell his grace,— Sing of Christ - mas time:— Born the

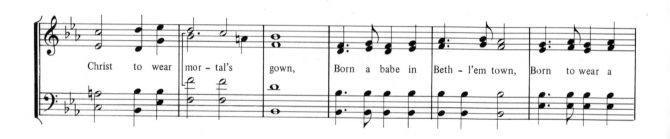

Christ to wear mor - tal's gown, Born a babe in Beth - l'em town, Born to wear a

mar - tyr's crown, Hal - le - lu - jah, Hal - le - lu - jah, Christ is born.

This carol may be sung in unison with piano, by SA or SAB choirs (accompanied or not) and by SSA (altos sing bass an octave up).

1 Praise God, tell his grace,
    Sing of Christmas time:
    Born the Christ to wear mortal's gown,
    Born a babe in Bethl'em town,
    Born to wear a martyr's crown,
    Hallelujah, Hallelujah, Christ is born.

2 Praise God, tell his grace,
    Sing of Eastertide:
    See the Christ die on Calvary's hill,
    For our sakes his role fulfil;
    Share disciples' Easter thrill,
    Hallelujah, Hallelujah, Christ alive.

3 Praise God, tell his grace,
    Sing of Pentecost:
    Feel the power which brings God's own peace,
    Comforter, our fears release,
    Justice, love and joy increase,
    Hallelujah, Hallelujah, Christ with us.

91

IF ONLY

Brian Frost (1935–)   *June Tillman (1943–)*

© 1980 Stainer & Bell Ltd

1 If only the bells of joy were ringing—were ringing,
  If only the people of God were singing—were singing
  Their hearts full of love,
  Their hearts full of love.

3 If only the pipes of peace were rising—were rising,
  If only the neighbours of God were surprising—surprising,
  Their hearts full of truth,
  Their hearts full of truth.

5 If only the music of Christ were playing—were playing,
  If only all the creatures on earth were saying—were saying
  We'll live in the Spirit,
  The gaiety of God.

2 If only the trumpets of faith were blowing—were blowing,
  If only the servants of God were showing—were showing
  Their hearts full of hope,
  Their hearts full of hope.

4 If only the drums of war were ceasing—were ceasing,
  If only our friendship with God was increasing—increasing,
  Our hearts full of grace,
  Our hearts full of grace.

6 If only the bells and trumpets together—together,
  If only the pipes and the drums were forever—forever,
  In tune with the Spirit,
  In tune with God's love.

7 If only the joy and the faith were abiding—abiding,
  If only the hope and the peace ceased their hiding—their hiding,
  There'd now be God with us,
  Emmanuel.

© 1980 Stainer & Bell Ltd

Optional instruments (preferably bells)

© 1980 Stainer & Bell Ltd

Crucifixion

92

THE TWELVE APOSTLES

Traditional Staffordshire
Arranged by R Vaughan Williams (1872–1958)

Traditional English

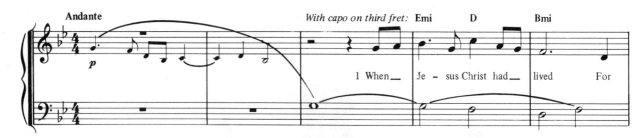

1 When__ Je - sus Christ had__ lived For

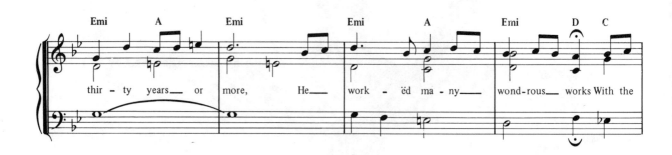

thir - ty years__ or more, He__ work - ëd ma - ny__ wond-rous__ works With the

twelve a - pos - tles pure.__ 2 Then__ Ju - das with the__ Jews__ Our

Sa - viour did__ be - tray,__ And__ un - to them, for__ thir - ty__ pence Je -

The verses should be adapted to meet the music with as little strain as possible. This version is for solo voice(s) and piano. The guitar chords are for use with unison singing without piano. An unaccompanied SATB arrangement, which may also be sung by choirs without tenors, is given overleaf with the remaining verses:

1 When Jesus Christ had lived
 For thirty years or more,
 He workëd many wondrous works
 With the twelve apostles pure.

2 Then Judas with the Jews
 Our Saviour did betray,
 And unto them, for thirty pence
 Jesus was sold away.

3 Then Judas sought a place
 With a tribe of armëd men,
 He bound his master fast in bands
 In whom there was no sin.

4 They led Him on straightway,
 Unto a judgement place;
 Without God's leave He was condemned
 To die in vile disgrace.

5 And for his garment then
 Brave soldiers did cast dice,
 It was a garment without seam
 And a jewel of great price.

6 They nailed his hands and feet
 And crowned his head with thorns,
 They gave him vinegar to drink
 But He the spongeful scorns.

7 Now all things seemed to mourn,
 When our blessëd Saviour died;
 The hills and rocks did rend in twain
 And the mountains did divide.

8 The heavens themselves grew dim,
 The moon forsook her light;
 And for three hours in one day
 It was a dismal sight.

9 At any Christmas time,
 Amongst good Christians all,
 This Christmas carol may be sung
 In any house or hall.

188

93

A TREE ONCE GREW IN GALILEE

Cecily Taylor (1930–) *Traditional, adapted John Maynard (1925–)*

© 1980 Stainer & Bell Ltd

1 A tree once grew in Galilee
 Where birds sang unafraid,
 And blossoms bloomed along each bough,
 The children loved its shade.

2 The tree grew strong in Galilee,
 But when the summer came
 The people tried to break it down
 With dark and deadly aim.

3 The blossoms fell, the birds had flown,
 Except for one white dove;
 They cut the branches like a cross
 To hang the Prince of Love.

4 Oh, there they hanged the Prince of Love
 And took him down for dead,
 But winter's hold was scarce three days,
 Then spring burst out instead.

5 New life burst out for joy again,
 The birds sang loud and free,
 While petals fell like blessings from
 That tree in Galilee:

6 And where they fall is healing love,
 Who climb it find new birth,
 Its roots can touch the hearts of men,
 Its branches span the earth, can span the earth.

94
SON OF MAN

Sydney Carter (1915–)

Sydney Carter (1915–)

If you are a son of man You
what will hap – pen when you die There

won – der where you're go – ing, And
is no way of

know – ing. They talk a – bout a

hea – ven And they talk a – bout a hell,_____ But wheth – er they are

right or not No son of man can tell. well. *rit.*

Instruments may add the top notes of the first two bars again until the first double bar; and again for the last four bars.

1 If you are a son of man
  You wonder where you're going,
  And what will happen when you die—
  There is no way of knowing.
  They talk about a heaven
  And they talk about a hell,
  But whether they are right or not
  No son of man can tell.

© 1965 Stainer & Bell Ltd

2 But if I were the Son of God,
  And if they crucified me,
  I'd think that I was luckier
  Than those who hung beside me,
  I'd know that I would rise again,
  And all things would be well,
  But when you are a son of man
  However can you tell?

3 If you are a son of man
  Then you can be mistaken;
  You hang upon the cross of doubt,
  You feel you are forsaken,
  And whether you will rise again
  Is more than you can tell—
  And if you were the son of man
  You've tasted this as well.

95

BITTER WAS THE NIGHT

Sydney Carter (1915—) *Sydney Carter (1915—)*

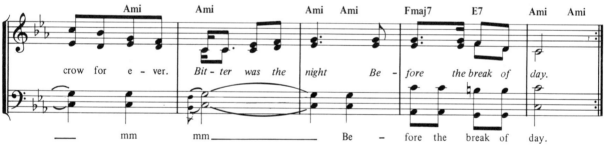

© 1964, 1980 Stainer & Bell Ltd

This carol may be sung in unison with keyboard or with guitar (in E minor). Two-part choirs may sing the top two parts unaccompanied or with piano; SAB sing parts as written; SSA altos sing bass part an octave higher.

NOTE: Words in italics are repeated in every verse.

1 Bitter was the night,
  Thought the cock would crow for ever.
  Bitter was the night
  Before the break of day.

2 Saw you passing by,
  Told them all I didn't know you ....

3 Told them all a lie,
  And I told it three times over ....

4 What did Judas do?
  Sold him for a bag of silver ....

5 What did Judas do?
  Hanged himself upon an alder ....

6 Bitter was the night,
  Thought there'd never be a morning ....

7 Bitter was the night,
  Thought the cock would crow for ever ....

© 1964 Stainer & Bell Ltd

Optional instruments

© 1980 Stainer & Bell Ltd

191

96

THE SEVEN VIRGINS

Traditional English

Traditional Herefordshire
Arranged by R Vaughan Williams (1872–1958)

© 1919 Stainer & Bell Ltd

The verses should be adapted to meet the music with as little strain as possible. This version is for solo voice(s) and piano. The guitar chords are for use with unison singing without piano. An unaccompanied SATB arrangement, which may also be sung by SSA (altos sing bass an octave higher) or SAB, is given opposite with the remaining verses.

1 Under the leaves, the leaves of life,
  There I saw virgins seven,
  And one of them was Mary mild,
  Was our Lord's mother from Heaven.

2 'O what are you seeking, you seven fair maids,
  All under the leaves of life?'
  'We're seeking for sweet Jesus Christ,
  To be our heavenly guide.'

3 'Go you down, go you down to yonder town,
  As far as you can see,
  And there you'll find sweet Jesus Christ
  With His body nailed to a tree.'

4 So they went down to yonder town
  As fast as foot could fall,
  And many a grievous bitter tear
  From the virgins' eyes did fall.

5 'Dear mother, do not weep for me,
  Your weeping doth Me grieve,
  O I must suffer this,' He said,
  'For Adam and for Eve.'

6 'O how can I my weeping leave
  Or my sorrows undergo
  Whilst I do see my own Son die,
  When sons I have no more?'

7 'Dear mother, dear mother, you must take John,
  All for to be your son,
  That he may be a comfort to you
  When I am dead and gone!

8 'O come, thou John Evangelist,
  Thou'rt welcome unto me,
  But more welcome my own dear Son
  That I bore from my own body.'

9 Then He laid his head on his right shoulder,
  Seeing death it struck Him nigh:
  'The Holy Ghost be with your soul,
  I die, dear mother, I die.'

10 Oh the rose, the rose, the gentle rose,
  The laurel that grows so green!
  May the Lord give us grace in every place
  To pray for our noble Queen.

193

97

THE MOON SHINES BRIGHT

Anonymous   *Traditional English*

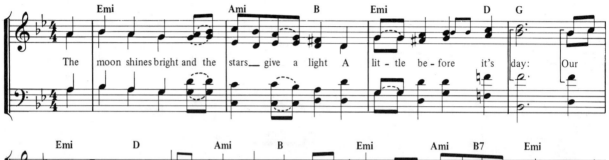

The moon shines bright and the stars give a light A little before it's day: Our

Lord, our God, he called on us, And bade us awake and pray.

This carol may be sung in unison with keyboard or with guitar (in E minor). Two-part choirs may sing the top two parts unaccompanied or with piano; SAB sing parts as shown; SSA altos sing bass part an octave higher. Take care with number of syllables in verses.

1 The moon shines bright and the stars give a light
   A little before it's day:
   Our Lord, our God, he called on us,
   And bade us awake and pray.

2 Awake, awake, good people all;
   Awake, and you shall hear,
   Our Lord, our God, died on the Cross
   For you he loved so dear.

3 A garland gay I've brought you here,
   And at your door it stands.
   It's nothing but a sprout but it's well spreaded out
   By the work of our poor hands.

4 The life of man is but a span,
   He flourishes like a flower.
   He's here today and tomorrow he's gone,
   And he's dead all in an hour.

5 And when you're dead and in your grave
   And covered over with clay,
   The worms shall eat your flesh, good man,
   And your bones shall mould away.

6 And the trees shall be green as the grass can grow,
   For from his glorious seat
   Our Lord, our God, will water them
   With the heavenly dew so sweet.

7 And for the saving of our souls
   Christ died upon the Cross;
   We ne'er shall do for Jesus Christ
   As he hath done for us.

8 And now our song is almost done
   And we can no longer stay,
   So bless you all both great and small
   And we wish you a joyful May.

Optional instruments

As this is an old dancer's tune, a drum may play ‖: ♩ ♫ ♩ ♫ :‖ *throughout.*

98

DEATH AND RESURRECTION

John Tearnan (1937—)   *David Evans (1940—)*

© 1974 Stainer & Bell Ltd

If preferred, verses 5 and 6 may continue in D minor.

1 Jesus in the garden,
Sad and left alone,
Soldiers come to take him;
His friends have run for home.

2 Jesus in the courtroom,
Sad and left alone,
People come to mock him
In robe and crown of thorns.

3 Jesus on the hillside,
Sad and left alone,
In the silent darkness
He dies there on his own.

4 Hiding in their home,
Disciples lock the door,
Frightened of the people;
They go outside no more.

5 Disciples in the room
Feel sadness turn to joy,
Know there's work for them to do,
Throw open wide the door.

6 Disciples meet the crowds
To share their joy with them,
Dance and sing to tell about
The man from Nazareth.

99

A CAROL FOR EASTER SATURDAY

Fred Pratt Green (1903—)

French, sixteenth century

Good neigh-bours, do not ask them why They hide their heads in shame, For

they have let their Mas-ter die, And dare not name his Name. It was but yes-ter-

-day he died: And who knows yet what shall be-tide?____ He who died

comes to reign! Je sus shall reign! On the Third Day rise a-gain!

1 Good neighbours, do not ask them why
They hide their heads in shame,
For they have let their Master die,
And dare not name his Name.
It was but yesterday he died:
And who knows yet what shall betide?
He who died comes to reign!
Jesus shall reign!
On the Third Day rise again!

2 His sad disciples feel their loss
Weigh on them like a stone;
The soldiers, taking down the cross,
Count one more duty done.
It was but yesterday he died:
And who knows yet what shall betide?
CHORUS

3 Today the promise falls apart;
The Kingdom does not come.
The Master died of broken heart,
And God himself is dumb.
It was but yesterday he died:
And who knows yet what shall betide?
CHORUS

4 On such a day, the Day Between,
When all your hopes have fled,
O put your trust in things unseen,
In love that is not dead.
Lift up your hearts, all you who grieve;
Be not despairing, but believe!
CHORUS

197

100

A GOD AND YET A MAN?

Text, fifteenth century,
adapted by John Kiteley

John Dowland (1563–1626)

© 1980 Stainer & Bell Ltd

Dowland wrote this tune to be sung with lute or in four parts. If singing in parts, take the first note within each beat as the next syllable.
Guitar chords may be used as shown in E minor.

1 A God, and yet a man?
  A maid, and yet a mother?
  Mind wonders what mind can
  Conceive one, or the other.

2 A God, yet can he die?
  A corpse, yet can he live?
  What mind can well reply?
  What reason reason give?

3 God's truth itself does teach it;
  Man's mind can only blunder;
  And reason cannot reach it.
  Believe—leave it to wonder.

101

EASTER DAY CAROL

Fred Pratt Green (1903–)

Traditional Burgundian

What tale is this our wo-men bring? Who can be-lieve so strange a thing? An emp-ty tomb? How can this be? Where he was laid, there surely he must be! Hur-ry, hur-ry, bro-thers; do not more de-lay; May-be it is true what the wo-men say!

© 1980 Stainer & Bell Ltd

In this carol, the author suggests that verses 1 and 2 may be sung by male voice(s), verses 3 and 4 by female voice(s) and the last (and all choruses) by everyone. In the spirit of the pipe and tabor which originally played the tune, a drum may play ♩ ♫ throughout, doubling the last three syllables to finish the carol.

1 What tale is this our women bring?
Who can believe so strange a thing?
An empty tomb? How can this be?
Where he was laid, there surely he must be!
Hurry, hurry, brothers; do not more delay;
Maybe it is true what the women say!

2 In this half-light, and half-awake,
What simple errors one may make;
And fond illusions give relief
To hearts that bear so great a weight of grief.
CHORUS

3 Pay we no heed to what he said,
Of how he talked of being dead,
And of those three mysterious days?
And did he not himself have power to raise?
CHORUS

4 Let Brother Peter, Brother John,
Whose word we can rely upon,
Seek out the truth, so we may know
Where Jesus, whom we loved, and love, is now.
CHORUS

5 They run, these two, and what they see
Shall be both truth and mystery:
For he, the Crucified, is risen,
No power on earth can silence or imprison.
CHORUS

102
LORD OF THE DANCE

Sydney Carter (1915–)

*Traditional Shaker Melody,
adapted by Sydney Carter (1915–)*

I danced in the morning When the world was be-gun, And I danced in the moon And the stars__ and the sun; And I came down from hea-ven And I danced on the earth, At Beth-le-hem I___ had my birth.

'Dance, then, wher-e-ver you may be, I am the Lord of the Dance,' said he, 'And I'll lead you all, wher-e-ver you may be, And I'll lead you all in the Dance,' said he.

An all-purpose version of this carol to be performed by any number of singers and players from solo singer with guitar to full choir and orchestra is available in score from Stainer & Bell Ltd.

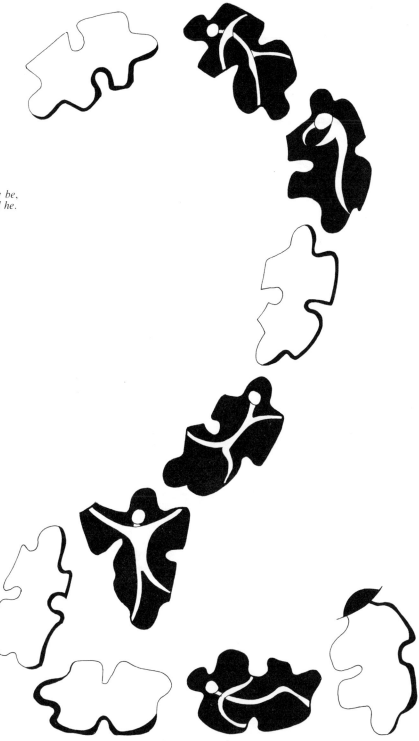

1 I danced in the morning
  When the world was begun,
  And I danced in the moon
  And the stars and the sun;
  And I came down from heaven
  And I danced on the earth,
  At Bethlehem
  I had my birth.
  'Dance then wherever you may be,
  I am the Lord of the Dance,' said he,
  'And I'll lead you all wherever you may be,
  And I'll lead you all in the Dance,' said he.

2 I danced for the scribe
  And the pharisee,
  But they would not dance
  And they wouldn't follow me.
  I danced for the fishermen,
  For James and John—
  They came with me
  And the dance went on.
  CHORUS

3 I danced on the Sabbath
  And I cured the lame;
  The holy people
  Said it was a shame.
  They whipped and they stripped
  And they hung me on high,
  And they left me there
  On a cross to die.
  CHORUS

4 I danced on a Friday
  When the sky turned black;
  It's hard to dance
  With the devil on your back.
  They buried my body
  And they thought I'd gone—
  But I am the Dance,
  And I still go on.
  CHORUS

5 They cut me down
  And I leapt up high;
  'I am the Life
  That'll never, never die.
  I'll live in you
  If you'll live in me;
  I am the Lord
  Of the Dance.' said he.
  CHORUS

103
NEW LIFE

June Tillman (1943—)   *June Tillman (1943—)*

Lyrics (melody line):
There is dark-ness in the night-time When the world is fast a-sleep;___ But the sun breaks through at morn-ing Af-ter soft re-fresh-ing sleep. Sing Ho--san-na, al-le-lu-ya, Out of dark-ness comes the light.

This carol may be sung in unison or solo with keyboard or with guitar. Unaccompanied verses may be sung by taking the two top parts of the right hand.

Optional instruments

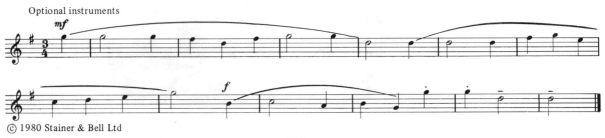

1 There is darkness in the night-time
  When the world is fast asleep;
  But the sun breaks through at morning
  After soft refreshing sleep.
  Sing Hosanna, alleluya,
  Out of darkness comes the light.

2 There is darkness in the garden
  When the seeds are buried deep;
  But in springtime comes awakening
  New life leaps from winter sleep.
  CHORUS

3 There was darkness in the city
  When the bombers thudded in;
  But a time came for rebuilding
  And for peace to reconcile.
  CHORUS

4 There is darkness in our living
  When the world seems parched and dry
  But deep down are springs of healing
  Welling up in time of need.
  CHORUS

5 There was darkness in the money
  Which betrayed the trust of friends,
  But the evening brought the laughter
  Of the food and drink that's shared.
  CHORUS

6 There was darkness in the greeting
  When his friends all ran away,
  There was still a time for healing
  And for hate turned into love.
  CHORUS

7 There was darkness in the courtroom
  When the crowd yelled out for blood,
  But the struggle up the hillside
  Brought a stranger's helping hand.
  CHORUS

8 There was darkness on the hillside
  When they killed the rebel king;
  But the evening brought a resting,
  Winding sheets in tomb of stone.
  CHORUS

9 There was darkness in the garden
  And the world seemed hushed in awe
  When the gravestone cracked right open
  And the tomb gave up its power.
  CHORUS

10 There was darkness in the weeping
  When they all thought he was dead;
  But the morning brought the gladness
  Of reunion with a friend.
  CHORUS

11 Out of night-time comes the sunrise;
  Out of winter comes the spring;
  Out of death there comes a rising,
  God has sent us his own Spring.
  CHORUS

104
I SING OF A KINGDOM

Cecily Taylor (1930–)

Lyn Howe (1951–)

204

205

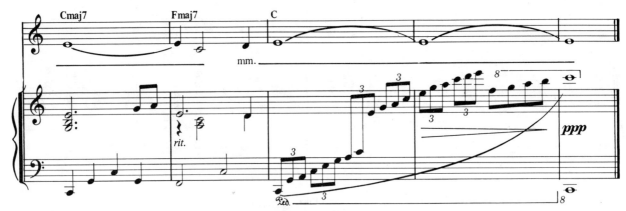

When this carol is sung by a group, divide at the fifth-time bar, some singing 'light' and some humming the coda.

1 I sing of a kingdom—
  A kingdom we share;
  Wherever there's loving,
  Whenever we care;
  A-ah, sing with me,
  A-ah, sing with me:
  And the sun on the garden
  Has chased away night,
  And the tomb is quite empty,
  Our hearts set alight, set alight.

2 I sing of a kingdom—
  The kingdom within,
  Where wrong is forgiven,
  New life can begin;
  A-ah, it is free,
  A-ah, it is free:
  CHORUS

3 I sing of a kingdom—
  The kingdom begun
  Where hatred is conquered
  And all men are one;
  A-ah, it can be,
  A-ah, it can be:
  CHORUS

4 I sing of a kingdom—
  Where grief is no more,
  With loved ones together
  And death but a door;
  A-ah, you will see,
  A-ah, you will see:
  CHORUS

5 I sing of a kingdom
  Where love is the king,
  And all we have given
  Is all we can bring;
  A-ah, sing with me,
  A-ah, sing with me:
  CHORUS

Alternative chorus if used at Christmas
  I will run with the shepherds,
  I'll go with the kings;
  Can you hear the earth singing
  The song that it brings, that it brings?

Lyn Howe (1951–)

Alternative chorus if used at Whitsun
  And the flame of the Spirit
  Is piercing the night
  Where the wind fans the loving
  Of hearts set alight, set alight.

105

IN VERNALI TEMPORE

Anonymous. English version
by Allen Percival (1925–)

Melody in 'Piae Cantiones' (1582)

With capo on 3rd fret

In— ver - na - li tem — po - re / Or - tu lae - ta bun — do.
Dum— re - ced — unt fri - go - ra, / Nun - ci - at hir - un — do.

Ter — rae, Mar — is, / Ne — mor - is, / Dec — us ad — est
Vi - gor red — it / cor - por - is, / Ced — it dol — or

De — for - is / re — no - va — to mun — do.
pec — tor - is, / Tem — po - re— ju - cun — do.

© 1980 Stainer & Bell Ltd

In vernali tempore
Ortu laeta bundo.
Dum recedunt frigora,
Nunciat hirundo.
Terrae, Maris, Nemoris,
Decus adest
Deforis renovato mundo.
Vigor redit corporis,
Cedit dolor pectoris,
Tempore jucundo.

NOTES:

ae = ay
re-ce-dunt = ray-shay-dunt
nun-ci-at = noon-she-at
ce-dit = shay-deet
j = y

English version

Now that spring is come anew,
Rivers rise with gladness
Freed from ice that stopped their flow.
Free their hearts from sadness,
Earth and seas and every tree
Look towards the light and see
All the world appearing.
Every creature springs to life.
Swallows bring an end to strife:
Youth's eternal Springtime.

Optional instruments

© 1980 Stainer & Bell Ltd

106

BIRD OF HEAVEN

Sydney Carter (1915–)   *Sydney Carter (1915–)*

Catch the bird of hea-ven,___ Lock him in a cage of gold;

Look a-gain to-morrow,___ And he will be gone. Ah! the bird of hea-ven!___

Fol-low where the bird has gone; Ah! the bird of hea-ven!___ Keep on trav-el-ling on.

Optional instruments or equal voice backing

Ah,___ Ah,___ Ah,___ Ah,___

___ Ah, Ah, Ah, Ah.

1 Catch the bird of heaven,
  Lock him in a cage of gold;
  Look again tomorrow,
  And he will be gone.
  Ah! the bird of heaven!
  Follow where the bird has gone;
  Ah! the bird of heaven!
  Keep on travelling on.

2 Lock him in religion,
  Gold and frankincense and myrrh
  Carry to his prison,
  But he will be gone.
  CHORUS

3 Temple made of marble,
  Beak and feather made of gold.
  All the bells are ringing,
  But the bird has gone.
  CHORUS

4 Bell and book and candle
  Cannot hold him any more,
  For the bird is flying
  As he did before.
  Ah! the bird of heaven!
  Follow where the bird has gone;
  If you want to find him,
  Keep on travelling on.

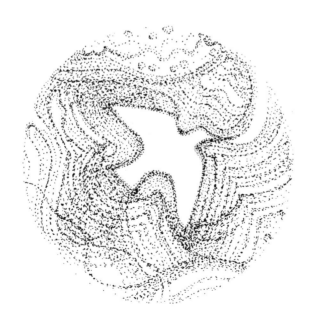

107

EASTER CAROL

Fred Pratt Green (1903–) *Ida Prins-Buttle (1908–)*

After darkness, light, After Win-ter, Spring; After dy-ing, life: Al – le – lu – ia!

1 After darkness, light;
After Winter, Spring;
After dying, life:
Alleluia!

2 Take his body down:
Lay it in the tomb;
Love has overcome:
Alleluia!

3 Turn away in grief;
Turn away in faith;
Celebrate his death:
Alleluia!

4 Come whatever may
God will have his way;
Welcome, Easter Day:
Alleluia!

Customs

108
GREEN GROWETH THE HOLLY

Anonymous

Henry VIII (1491–1547)

© 1980 Stainer & Bell Ltd

Originally for ATT, this carol may be sung by TBarB transposing down a fourth. Alternatively two voices only sing the top stave with an instrument playing the alto and a drum repeating the rhythm ♩ ♫ throughout.

109

THE CAROL OF THE FLOWERS

Anonymous   *French, seventeenth century*

Sweet-est flowers, O come and in a beau-teous ring, Spread your love-ly perfumes round your heavenly King.

Ti-ny Vio-let, em-blem of all mo-des-ty, Show how hum-ble He is made for you and me. Sweet-est

This carol may be sung in unison with piano or with guitar. Two-part choirs may sing the top parts unaccompanied or with piano; SAB sing parts as shown.

Sweetest flowers, O come and in a beauteous ring,
Spread your lovely perfumes round your heavenly King.

1 Tiny Violet, emblem of all modesty,
   Show how humble He is made for you and me.
   CHORUS

2 Lovely Lily, emblem of all purity,
   He is born of Mary, who is pure as thee.
   CHORUS

3 Little Crocus, glowing all with colour bright,
   See He glows more lovely with a heavenly light.
   CHORUS

4 Sweetest Rose, thou emblem of eternal love,
   Thus He draws us all with Him to heaven above.
   CHORUS

Optional instruments

110

A LOVERS' CAROL

Fred Pratt Green (1903–)

Traditional Burgundian

The first verse may be repeated at the end, either by the original voice or by all three singers.

All sing:

1 I saw two lovers, in the Spring,
  A-kissing and a-quarrelling,
  And this strange carol heard them sing,
  Forgiving
  Each other,
  And prayed God's grace they would not love another.

She sings:

2 I love the angry looks I get
  When I'm unkind and you're upset;
  I only hope you won't forget
  I love you,
  I love you!
  Oh, in my heart I shall forever love you!

He sings:

3 See how your cherry lips are set
  When I'm upstage and you're upset;
  I only hope you won't forget
  I love you,
  I love you!
  Oh, in my heart I shall forever love you!

The lovers sing together:

4 We'll go to church, with wedding bells,
  With you (me) in white and me (you) in tails,
  Or run away, if all else fails,
  Together,
  Together!
  And never, never cease to be together.

111

DECK THE HALL

Anonymous   *Traditional Welsh*

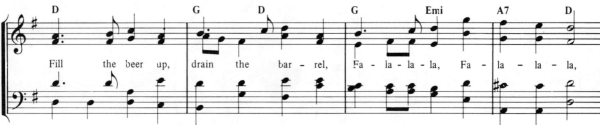

This carol may be sung in unison with keyboard or with guitar. Two-part choirs may sing the top two parts with piano; SAB sing parts as shown; SSA altos sing bass part in lines 1 and 4, tenor part in line 3. The original melody is in the alto of the last two chords.

1 Deck the hall with boughs of holly,
  Fa-la-la-la-la, Fa-la-la-la,
  'Tis the season to be jolly,
  Fa-la-la-la-la, Fa-la-la-la.
  Fill the beer up, drain the barrel,
  Fa-la-la-la-la, Fa-la-la-la,
  Troll the ancient Christmas carol,
  Fa-la-la-la-la, Fa-la-la-la.

2 See the flowing bowl before us,
  Fa-la-la-la-la, Fa-la-la-la,
  Strike the harp and join the chorus,
  Fa-la-la-la-la, Fa-la-la-la,
  Follow me in merry measure,
  Fa-la-la-la-la, Fa-la-la-la,
  While I sing of beauty's treasure,
  Fa-la-la-la-la, Fa-la-la-la.

3 Fast away the old year passes,
  Fa-la-la-la-la, Fa-la-la-la,
  Hail the new, ye lads and lassies,
  Fa-la-la-la-la, Fa-la-la-la,
  Laughing, quaffing all together,
  Fa-la-la-la-la, Fa-la-la-la,
  Heedless of the wind and weather,
  Fa-la-la-la-la, Fa-la-la-la.

Optional instruments

112
CANDLEMAS EVE

Robert Herrick (1591–1674)

Adapted from William Lawes (1602–1645)

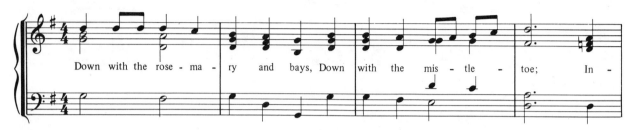

1 Down with the rosemary and bays,
  Down with the mistletoe;
  Instead of holly, now upraise
  The greener box, for show.

2 The holly hitherto did sway:
  Let box now domineer
  Until the dancing Easter day,
  Or Easter's eve appear.

3 Then youthful box, which now hath grace
  Your houses to renew,
  Grown old, surrender must his place
  Unto the crispëd yew.

4 When yew is out, then birch comes in,
  And many flowers beside,
  Both of a fresh and fragrant kin,
  To honour Whitsuntide.

5 Green rushes then, and sweetest bents,
  With cooler oaken boughs,
  Come in for comely ornaments,
  To readorn the house.

6 Thus times do shift;
  Each thing his turn does hold;
  New things succeed,
  As former things grow old.

NOTE: 'Bents' = bent grass

Verse 6 (Keyboard plays as written above)

113

HOPSA LISELLA

Traditional Alsace
English words by Joy Hyman and Jennifer Rice

Traditional Alsace

This carol may be sung in unison or in two parts with guitar, or with keyboard playing the upper stave only (an octave higher throughout, using both hands if it helps).

1 Hopsa Lisella, hopsa Lisella
Lipft dar fuas zum dansa;
Sautez Lisella, sautez Lisella
Lève le pied pour danser.
Nous irons dimanche
A la maison blanche,
Toi z'en nan-kin,
Moi z'en ba-zin,
Tous deux en escarpins.

2 Tremp' ton pain, Marie, tremp' ton pain, Marie,
Tremp' ton pain dans le sauce,
Tremp' ton pain, Marie, tremp' ton pain, Marie,
Tremp' ton pain dans le vin.
Nous ferons des crèpes,
Puisque c'est la fête,
J'en mangerai,
T'en mangerai,
Tout le monde y en aura.

NOTE: The original words mix the German dialect of the vineyards with French. 'Hopsa' is common to all German wine-growing areas *cf.* 'Heysa, hopsa' in Haydn's 'The Seasons'.

219

114

SHROVE TUESDAY CAROL

Fred Pratt Green (1903–)

Traditional Burgundian

So toss, toss, toss the gol-den pan-cake, Wash it down with ale:_____ The on - ly

thing that we can take To heaven's a ran-somed soul! Friends, we be-gin to-mor - row The

for - ty days of Lent: To-day we'll ban-ish sor - row, And feast to our con - tent:

*To end the carol, repeat from * to * in verse 3, with a slight pulling back. SA choirs may sing the right hand part, altos taking the rhythm of sopranos throughout.*

NOTE: In medieval times, the day before Ash Wednesday (the first day of Lent) came to be known as Shrove Tuesday or Pancake Day. On this day Christians were 'shriven' (confessed their sins and received absolution) in preparation for Lent; but it was also a day of feasting before enforced abstinence, hence the pancakes. The popular attitude to the day is recaptured in this modern carol.

So, toss, toss, toss the golden pancake,
Wash it down with ale:
The only thing that we can take
To heaven's a ransomed soul!

1 Friends, we begin tomorrow
 The forty days of Lent:
 Today we'll banish sorrow,
 And feast to our content:
 CHORUS

2 Tomorrow we shall mourn them,
 Our pleasure-loving ways,
 Give up our sins or pawn them,
 And fill our mouths with praise:
 CHORUS

3 Tomorrow, meekly shriven,
 We'll turn our backs on hell,
 Resume our path to heaven,
 And know that all is well:
 CHORUS (*repeat last line*)

© 1980 Stainer & Bell Ltd

Optional instruments

115
PACE-EGGING SONG

Anonymous English, nineteenth century

*English ballad tune,
nineteenth century*

Here's two or three jolly boys all in one mind, We've come a-pace-egging and we hope you'll be kind. We hope you'll prove kind with your eggs and strong beer, And we'll come no more nigh you until the next year. Fol de rid-dle rol, fol de ra, Fol de rid-dle dol de day.

Guitar chords are for use when guitars alone are accompanying; the bracketed chords in the higher key are easier to play.

1 Here's two or three jolly boys all in one mind,
   We've come a-pace-egging and we hope you'll be kind.
   We hope you'll prove kind with your eggs and strong beer,
   And we'll come no more nigh you until the next year.
   Fol de riddle dol, fol de ra, Fol de riddle dol de day.

2 The first that comes in is Lord Collingwood,
   He fought with Lord Nelson till he shed his blood.
   He put in his sword, he drew it no more;
   We hope you'll prove honest wherever you are.
   CHORUS

3 The next that comes in is Lord Nelson, you see,
   With a bunch of blue ribbons tied down to his knee;
   And the star on his breast like silver do shine,
   And we hope you'll remember it's pace egging time.
   CHORUS

4 The next that comes in is our Jolly Jack Tar,
   He sailed with Lord Nelson all through the last war.
   He's arrived from the sea old England to view,
   And he's come a-pace-egging with our jovial crew.
   CHORUS

5 The next that comes in is Tom Tosspot, you see,
   A valiant old fellow in every degree.
   He's a valiant old man and he wears a pigtail
   And all his delight is in drinking mulled ale.
   CHORUS

6 The next that comes in is old miser Brownbags,
   For fear of her money she wears her old rags.
   She's gold and she's silver all laid up in store
   And she's come a-pace-egging in hopes to get more.
   CHORUS

7 So ladies and gen'lemen that sit by the fire,
   Put your hands in your pockets, that's all we desire.
   Put your hands in your pockets and pull out your purse;
   And give us a trifle, you'll not be much worse.
   CHORUS

8 If you can drink one glass, then we can drink two;
   Here's a health to Victoria, the same unto you.
   Do mind what you're doing and see that all's right:
   If you give naught we take naught; farewell and goodnight.
   CHORUS

NOTE: This is an early Victorian Easter visiting carol with the
named characters coming in with each verse dressed up like
the 'mummers'. Pace Eggs were hard-boiled eggs painted
with 'humpty-dumpty' figures or any decorations and could
be broken against each other in competition as in the harvest
game of 'conkers'.

116
MAY DAY CAROL

Anonymous

Traditional Cornish

Optional instruments

NOTE: This song is used in celebrations in Helston, Cornwall on their Furry (Fair) Day, a May day on which they bring Spring gladness to each house in the town. The dance, performed in couples, uses three running steps and a hop in each bar. In the first eight bars they move forward together; in the first four bars of the chorus each couple dances clockwise in its own circle with right hands across (pin-wheel fashion); in the last four bars they do the same in reverse. The 'Halan To' is the garland of May flowers that they carry.

1 We have been rambling half the night
   And almost all the day-a,
   And now returned back again,
   We've brought you a branch of may-a,
   With 'Halan To', sing merry O,
   With 'Halan To', sing merry.

2 Robin Hood and Little John,
   They both are gone to fare, O,
   And we will to the greenwood go,
   To see what they do there, O,
   CHORUS

3 We were up as soon as day
   To fetch the summer home, O,
   The summer is a-coming on
   And winter is a gone, O,
   CHORUS

4 Those Frenchmen that make such a boast,
   They shall eat the grey-goose feather, O,
   And we will eat up all the roast,
   In every land where'er we go,
   CHORUS

5 Saint George next shall be our song,
   Saint George he was a knight, O,
   Of all the kings in Christendom
   King Georgy is the right, O,
   CHORUS

6 Bless Aunt Mary with power and might,
   God send us peace in merry England,
   Pray send us peace both day and night,
   For evermore in merry England,
   CHORUS

7 Then let us all most merry be,
   And sing with cheerful voice-a;
   For we have good occasion now,
   This time for to rejoice-a,
   CHORUS

Sometimes the following alternative chorus
is sung after verse 2:

   And for to chase the buck and doe,
   To chase the buck and doe, O
   And for to chase the buck and doe,
   With 'Halan To', sing merry, O.

117

A HERB CAROL

Fred Pratt Green (1903–)   *John Dowland (1563–1626)*

When God cre - a - ted herbs He gave them work____ to do: Sweet Mar - jo - ram has fla - vour, Ber - ga - mot____ has frag - rance, Rose - ma - ry____ cures____ head-aches (And these____ are but a few); Then Sa - tan plant - ed Rue. When____ God____ cre - a - ted herbs, Then Sa - tan planted Rue, The____ sad mys - ter - ious Rue.

The music is a transcription of Dowland's lutesong 'Now cease my wandering eyes' (1600) incorporating the tune. As with the Elizabethan lyrics, these words should be sung freely across the bar-lines within their natural pronounciation.

NOTE: The common rue (*Ruta graveolens*) has long had a double reputation. The plant was much used in medieval times as a stimulative and irritant drug. It was commonly supposed to be used by witches. From its association with 'rue' (sorrow, repentance), the plant was also known as the 'herb of grace'. For the purpose of this medieval-style carol I have made rue a bad thing! (F.P.G.)

1 When God created herbs
 He gave them work to do:
 Sweet Marjoram has flavour,
 Bergamot has fragrance,
 Rosemary cures headaches
 (And these are but a few);
 Then Satan planted Rue.
 When God created herbs,
 Then Satan planted Rue,
 The sad, mysterious Rue.

2 So Eve made use of herbs
 That in her garden grew:
 Sweet Marjoram for flavour,
 Bergamot for fragrance,
 Rosemary for headaches
 (And these were but a few);
 But she was piercèd through.
 So Eve made use of herbs,
 But she was piercèd through
 When Adam plucked the Rue.

3 Our Lady loved the herbs
 That in her garden grew:
 Sweet Marjoram for flavour,
 Bergamot for fragrance,
 Rosemary for headaches
 (And these were but a few);
 But she was piercèd through.
 Our Lady loved the herbs,
 But she was piercèd through
 When Jesus plucked the Rue.

4 All you who dote on herbs
 And praise the good they do:
 Sweet Marjoram for flavour,
 Bergamot for fragrance,
 Rosemary for headaches
 (And these are but a few);
 Lest you be piercèd through.
 All you who dote on herbs,
 Lest you be piercèd through,
 Let none you love touch Rue.

118
THE PLOUGHSHARE

Traditional English
Collected by Jim Copper

Traditional English
Arranged by Jim Copper

The sun has gone down and the sky it looks red Down
on my soft pillow where I lay my head, When I
open my eyes for to see the stars shine Then the
thoughts of my true love run into my mind.

Reprinted by permission of William Heinemann Ltd from 'A Song for Every Season' by Bob Copper

This carol may be sung by a soloist or in unison with keyboard or with guitar. SA choirs sing top two parts accompanied or unaccompanied; SSA altos sing tenor part; tenors and basses in SATB or SAB repeat long notes where necessary in the rhythm of the words.

Optional Instruments

1 The sun has gone down and the sky it looks red
  Down on my soft pillow where I lay my head,
  When I open my eyes for to see the stars shine
  Then the thoughts of my true love run into my mind.

2 The sap has gone down and the leaves they do fall,
  To hedging and ditching our farmers they'll call.
  We will trim up their hedges, we will cut down their wood
  And the farmers they'll all say our faggots run good.

3 Now hedging being over, then sawing draws near,
  We will send for the sawyer the woods for to clear.
  And after he has sawed them and tumbled them down
  Then there he will flaw them all on the cold ground.

4 When sawing is over, then seedtime comes round,
  See our teams they are already preparing the ground,
  Then the man with his seed-lip, he'll scatter the corn,
  Then the harrows they will bury it to keep it from harm.

5 Now seedtime being over, then haying draws near,
  With our scythes, rakes and pitch-forks those meadows
                                            to clear.
  We will cut down their grass, boys, and carry it away,
  We will first call it green grass and then call it hay.

6 When haying is over, then harvest draws near,
  We will send to our Brewer to brew us strong beer,
  And in brewing strong beer, boys, we will cut down their corn
  And we'll take it to the barn, boys, to keep it from harm.

7 Now harvest being over bad weather comes on,
  We will send for the thresher to thresh out our corn.
  His hand-staff he'll handle, his swingel he'll swing,
  Till the very next harvest we'll all meet again.

8 Now since we have brought this so cheerfully around
  We will send for the jolly ploughman to plough up the ground.
  See the boy with his whip and the man to his plough
  Here's a health to the jolly ploughmen that plough up
                                            the ground.

NOTE:

After the singing the leading caroller should be given a glass with which to say:

'*Here's success to the bright ploughshare and may it never rust*'

to which the company should reply:

'*May the ploughshare never rust*'

Reprinted by permission of William Heinemann Ltd from 'A Song for Every Season' by Bob Copper.

119

A CONCERT-GOERS' CAROL

Fred Pratt Green (1903–)   *Traditional Basque*

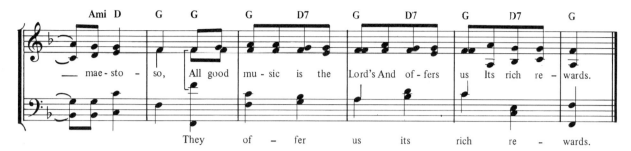

1 Turo, luro, luro, who can measure
 All that music can impart?
 Music gives unbounded pleasure
 To the listening mind and heart.
 In music's range
 The smallest change
 In pace or key
 Can suddenly
 Enchant us, enchant us.
 These are moments of delight all the great composers grant us:
 Giocoso,
 Or maestoso,
 All good music is the Lord's,
 And offers us
 Its rich rewards.

2 Turo, luro, luro, what a rondo!
 What a strange, exciting beat!
 How its final grand crescendo
 Gets us tapping with our feet!
 Relaxed, at ease,
 And quiet, please,
 Good people all,
 Who fill this hall,
 Discover, discover
 No one has to read the score to become a music-lover.
 None shall name us
 Ignoramus
 If our pleasure is sincere,
 And makes us want
 To stand and cheer.

3 Turo, luro, luro, brave conductor,
 Tackling something new and hard;
 He must know it tastes like nectar
 Only to the avant-garde.
 If what you hear
 Insults the ear,
 Forget the noise
 And hear the voice
 Of reason, of reason:
 What displeases you tonight, you may learn to love next season!
 Some disasters
 Turn out masters.
 All good music is the Lord's;
 But who can say
 What he applauds?

NOTE: Tenors and Basses sing the following:

1 Turo, luro, luro, luro,
 The smallest change in pace or range
 Enchants us, enchants us.
 So great composers grant us:
 Giocoso or maestoso
 They offer us its rich rewards.

2 Turo, luro, luro, luro,
 Relaxed, at ease, and quiet, please
 Discover, discover!
 Become a music lover.
 None shall name us Ignoramus
 It makes us want to stand and cheer.

3 Turo, luro, luro, luro,
 If what you hear insults the ear
 Of reason, of reason
 You may well love next season!
 Some disasters turn out masters.
 But who can say what he applauds?

120

THE FALL OF THE YEAR

Fred Pratt Green (1903–)   *Traditional French*

Sum - mer is o - ver; the dark fields lie fal - low;
See how the pop - lar turns o - range and yel - low!
All o - ther sea - sons have
ca - rols to spare: What shall we sing in the fall of the year?

1 Summer is over; the dark fields lie fallow;
  See how the poplar turns orange and yellow!
  All other seasons have carols to spare:
  What shall we sing in the fall of the year?

2 Morning and evening there's mist in the valley;
  Wine-red the berries on hawthorn and holly.
  Hark to the robin, how plaintive his air!
  What shall we sing in the fall of the year?

3 Newcomers forage in pasture and furrow;
  Squirrels are hoarding their food for tomorrow;
  Harvests are gathered: the autumn is here,
  Season of fruitfulness, fall of the year.

4 Sing of fulfilment, contentment, reflection;
  Sing, beyond winter, of earth's resurrection.
  Sing we this carol, now autumn is here:
  Thanks be to God for the fall of the year!

Optional instruments

This carol may be sung in unison with keyboard (playing small notes) or with guitar. It may also be sung unaccompanied, with or without the optional instrumental line, by SA, SAT, SAB, SATB as written. SSA choirs should sing SAB parts, taking the bass up one octave.

121

HALLOWE'EN CAROL

Anonymous   *Traditional English*

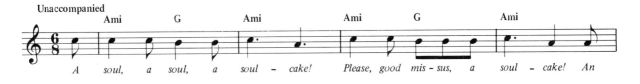

A soul, a soul, a soul – cake! Please, good mis-sus, a soul – cake! An

ap-ple, a pear, a plum and a cher-ry, A-ny good thing to make us all mer-ry,

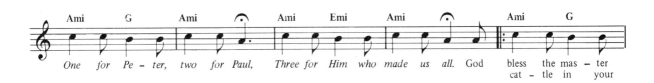

One for Pe-ter, two for Paul, Three for Him who made us all. God bless the mas-ter
cat-tle in your

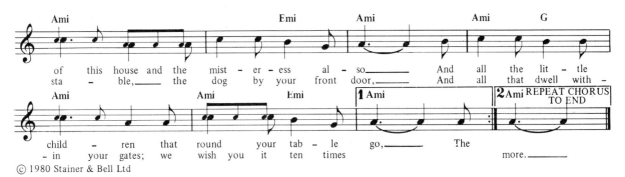

of this house and the mist-er-ess al-so,___ And all the lit-tle
sta-ble,___ the dog by your front door,___ And all that dwell with-

child – ren that round your tab – le go,___ The
– in your gates; we wish you it ten times   more.___

This carol, with its children's 'jingle' tune, sings of begging cakes to feed the souls of the departed who may visit again on Hallowe'en.

Optional accompaniments, ostinato throughout.

122

ALL HALLOW'S EVE

David Medd (1951–)   *David Medd (1951–)*

All ___ Hal - low's Eve, All ___ Hal - low's ___ Eve,

What I ___ saw I ___ can't ___ be - lieve, ___ This Oc - to - ber night on All Hal-low's Eve.

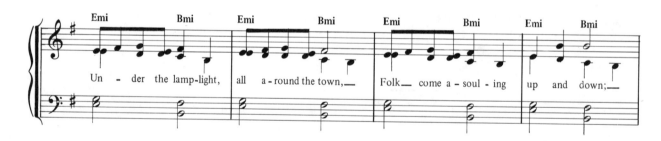

Un - der the lamp-light, all a - round the town, ___ Folk ___ come a - soul - ing up and down; ___

Who's that a - walk - ing un - der the trees, ___ This Oc - to - ber night on All Hal-low's Eve?

© 1980 Stainer & Bell Ltd

This carol may be sung by a soloist or in unison with keyboard or guitars. Unaccompanied verses may be sung by SA, SAT or SAB choirs; tenors and basses sing 'Oh' in wailing fashion from bars 9 to 12.

234

All Hallow's Eve,
All Hallow's Eve,
What I saw I can't believe,
This October night on All Hallow's Eve.

1 Under the lamplight, all around the town,
  Folk come a-souling up and down;
  Who's that a-walking under the trees,
  This October night on All Hallow's Eve?
  CHORUS

2 The moon she is up and the wind is on the hill,
  Of meat and drink we'll have our fill;
  Who's that a-singing on the breeze,
  This October night on All Hallow's Eve?
  CHORUS

3 Lonely people passing to and fro,
  Looking for a friend on the Earth below;
  Only the children listen to the breeze,
  This October night on All Hallow's Eve.
  CHORUS

4 Who can see the shadows on the grass?
  Who can hear the secret people pass?
  Who goes to wait by the rugged oak tree?
  This October night on All Hallow's Eve.
  CHORUS

NOTE: In verse 2 the first word in each of the first two lines should be sung on an up-beat 'B'.

235

123
BONFIRE CAROL

David Medd (1951–)   *David Medd (1951–)*

Re-member, re-member the Fifth of No-vem-ber, The night was dark and cold: Mis-ter

Fawkes took a torch to the House of West-min-ster In the dear, sad days of old.

Long be-fore the fires___ burned At vil-lage, farm and hill; Win-ter grew with ev-ery day, The

nights were dark and chill Up — on the eve of Sa-main When the sun grew red and old,

* D sharp last chorus only.

Fire—rose on ev-ery hand To warm the Winter's cold. *Re -* | Rockets fill the night with stars And all the children shout. *Re -*

Remember, remember the Fifth of November,
The night was dark and cold:
Mister Fawkes took a torch to the House of Westminster
In the dear, sad days of old.

1 Long before, the fires burned
  At village, farm and hill;
  Winter grew with every day,
  The nights were dark and chill—
  Upon the eve of Samain
  When the sun grew red and old,
  Fire rose on every hand
  To warm the Winter's cold.
  CHORUS

2 In the reign of James the First,
  Folk with him disagreed,
  To blow up Parliament they planned—
  A most uncivil deed!
  And Catesby and Company, set
  Gunpowder below,
  But poor Guy Fawkes was caught and hung
  As everybody knows.
  CHORUS

3 Catherine Wheels are turning,
  Roman Candles light the sky,
  Volcanoes fill the night with
  Coloured mountains heavens high;
  Silver Fountains, Golden Rain,
  Thunderclaps ring out,
  Rockets fill the night with stars
  And all the children shout.
  CHORUS

124

ADVENT CANDLES

Emily Chisholm (1910–)

Traditional Welsh

© 1980 Stainer & Bell Ltd

This carol may be sung in unison with keyboard or with guitar. Two-part choirs may sing the top two parts unaccompanied or with piano;
SAB sing parts as shown; SSA altos sing tenor part.

1 The holly and the ivy
  Are dancing in a ring,
  Round the berry-bright red candles
  And the white and shining King.

2 Oh, one is for the prophets
  And for the light they bring.
  They are candles in the darkness,
  All alight for Christ the King.

3 And two for John the Baptist.
  He calls on us to sing:
  'O prepare the way for Jesus Christ,
  He is coming, Christ the King.'

4 And three for Mother Mary.
  'I cannot see the way,
  But you promise me a baby.
  I believe you. I obey.'

5 And four are for God's people
  In every age and day.
  We are watching for his coming.
  We believe and we obey.

6 And Christ is in the centre,
  For this is his birthday,
  With the shining nights of Christmas
  Singing, 'He has come today.'

© 1972 Stainer & Bell Ltd

Optional voices or instruments (vv. 2-5). Sing 'One is for...', 'Two for John...' and so on.

The third line in each verse is sung by the main body of singers.

© 1979 Stainer & Bell Ltd

124a

THE HOLLY AND THE IVY

NOTE: When singing these words the tune opposite is used for both verse and chorus.

1 The holly and the ivy,
  When they are both full grown,
  Of all the trees that are in the wood,
  The holly bears the crown:
  The rising of the sun
  And the running of the deer,
  The playing of the merry organ,
  Sweet singing in the choir.

2 The holly bears a blossom,
  As white as the lily flower,
  And Mary bore sweet Jesus Christ,
  To be our sweet Saviour:
  CHORUS

3 The holly bears a berry,
  As red as any blood,
  And Mary bore sweet Jesus Christ
  To do poor sinners good:
  CHORUS

4 The holly bears a prickle,
  As sharp as any thorn,
  And Mary bore sweet Jesus Christ
  On Christmas day in the morn:
  CHORUS

5 The holly bears a bark,
  As bitter as any gall,
  And Mary bore sweet Jesus Christ
  For to redeem us all:
  CHORUS

6 The holly and the ivy,
  When they are both full grown,
  Of all the trees that are in the wood,
  The holly bears the crown:
  CHORUS

Traditional Gloucestershire

125
THE WREN SONG

Collected by Mrs Hoskins,
County Cork 1923

Traditional Irish

The wren, the wren, the king of all birds, Saint Steph-en's day was caught in the furze; Al-though he's lit-tle, his

fa-mi-ly's great. Rise up Mis-ter ...... and give us a trate. Hol-ler, hol-ler, hol-ler boys.

Optional instruments

240

NOTE: Verses 1 and 5 are addressed to the master of the house.

1 The wren, the wren, the king of all birds,
  Saint Stephen's day was caught in the furze;
  Although he's little, his family's great.
  Rise up Mister....and give us a trate.
  Holler, holler, holler boys.

2 We followed the wren three miles or more,
  Three miles or more, three miles or more,
  Through hedges and ditches and heaps of snow,
  At six o'clock in the morning.
  Holler, holler, holler boys.

3 Rolley, Rolley, where's your nest?
  It's in the bush that I love best,
  It's in the bush, the holly tree,
  Where all the boys do follow me.
  Holler, holler, holler boys.

4 Between my finger and my thumb
  There rose a blister as big as a plum;
  'Twas neither a plum or neither a cherry,
  But three, four shillings would make us merry.
  Holler, holler, holler boys.

5 Mister....is a worthy man
  And to his house we brought the wren,
  We brought the wren to play him a tune
  That he may be happy on Christmas noon.
  Holler, holler, holler boys.

6 As I went up a grand walk
  I saw a wren upon a stalk;
  I up with my stick and I hit a slap
  And I knocked him into the brandy shop.
  Holler, holler, holler boys.

7 I have a little box under my arm
  And three or four shillings would do it no harm.
  Up with the kettle and down with the pan,
  Give us our answer and let us be gone.
  Holler, holler, holler boys.

Spoken
All silver and no brass,
We are the boys that carry the cash.

Reprinted by permission of the English Folk Dance and Song Society.

241

126
CHRISTMAS'S LAMENTATION

Anonymous English (Elizabethan or Jacobean)　　　　*Court Ballad Tune, English Seventeenth Century*

This carol may be sung solo or in unison with keyboard or with guitar. Two-part choirs may sing the top two parts with keyboard; SAB sing as shown; SSA altos sing bass part an octave higher.

NOTE: These are the first three verses only of a long 'political' carol complaining that, in the reign of James I, the nobility all flocked to Court in London and forsook their country houses. At Christmas, 1622, James issued a proclamation that they should spend it in the country. The full text is in W. Chappell, 'Popular Music of the Olden Time'.

1 Christmas is my name, far have I gone,
  Have I gone, have I gone, have I gone without regard;
  Whereas great men by flocks there be flown,
  There be flown, there be flown, there be flown to Londonward.
  There they in pomp and pleasure do waste
  That which old Christmas was wonted to feast,
  Well-a-day! well-a-day. Well-a-day, where should I stay?
  Houses where music was wont for to ring,
  Nothing but bats and owlets do sing,
  Well-a-day! well-a-day. Well-a-day, where should I stay?

2 Christmas beef and bread is turn'd into stones,
  Into stones, into stones, into stones and silken rags;
  And Lady Money sleeps and makes moans,
  And makes moans, and makes moans, and makes moans in|misers' bags:
  Houses where pleasure once did abound,
  Nought but a dog and a shepherd is found,
  Well-a-day! well-a-day. Well-a-day, where should I stay?
  Places where Christmas revels did keep
  Are now become habitations for sheep.
  Well-a-day! well-a-day. Well-a-day, where should I stay?

3 Philemon's cottage was turned into gold,
  Into gold, into gold, for harbouring Jove:
  Rich men their houses up for to keep,
  For to keep, for to keep, for to keep might their|greatness move;
  But in the city, they say, they do live,
  Where gold by handfuls away they do give:
  I'll away. I'll away. I'll away, for here's no stay.
  And thither, therefore, I purpose to pass
  Hoping at London to find the gold ass:
  I'll away. I'll away. I'll away, for here's no stay.

NOTE: In verse 3, lines 1 and 3 begin with the rhythm

Optional instruments

127

CAROL FOR NEW YEAR'S DAY

Anonymous English, 1642, called
'The Waits' Carol'

Melody from William Ballet's Lute Book
c. 1600 and 'The Dancing Master', 1686

The old year now a-way is fled, The new year it is en-ter-ëd; Then

let us now our sins down-tread, And joy-ful-ly all ap-pear: Let's

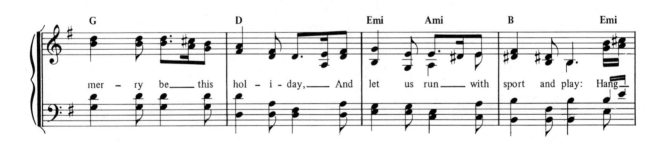

mer-ry be this hol-i-day, And let us run with sport and play: Hang

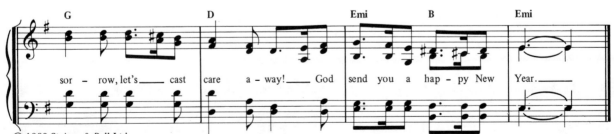

sor-row, let's cast care a-way! God send you a hap-py New Year.

© 1980 Stainer & Bell Ltd

This carol is best sung by a soloist with keyboard or with guitar but verses may be sung by SA and the second half by SAB or SATB groups unaccompanied.

1 The old year now away is fled,
  The new year it is enterëd;
  Then let us now our sins down-tread,
  And joyfully all appear:
  Let's merry be this holiday,
  And let us run with sport and play:
  Hang sorrow, let's cast care away!
  God send you a happy New Year!

2 And now with New Year's gifts each friend
  Unto each other they do send:
  God grant we may all our lives amend,
  And that the truth may appear.
  Now, like the snake, cast off your skin
  Of evil thoughts and wicked sin,
  And to amend this new year begin:
  God send us a merry New Year!

Optional instruments

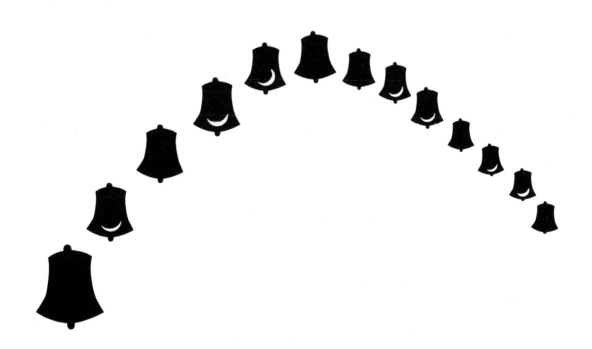

Index

Composers and Arrangers

Poets and Translators

Index of First Lines

Titles

Printed in Great Britain by Galliard (Printers) Ltd, Great Yarmouth